GCSE OCR Double Award
Applied Science
The Study Guide

This book is for anyone doing **GCSE OCR Applied Science (Double Award)** at foundation level.

GCSE Applied Science is all about **experiencing science**.
But more than that — it means **understanding** the role of scientists in the
real world by actually **doing the science yourself**.

And you can't do that without a fair chunk of **background knowledge**. Hmm, tricky.

Happily this CGP book includes all the **science facts** you need to learn,
and shows you how they work in the **real world**. Not only that, we've given you
loads of **handy advice** for doing **practicals** and getting stuck into those **reports**.
And in true CGP style, we've explained it all as **clearly and concisely** as possible.

It's also got some daft bits in to try and make the
whole experience at least vaguely entertaining for you.

What CGP is all about

Our sole aim here at CGP is to produce the highest
quality books — carefully written, immaculately presented
and dangerously close to being funny.

Then we work our socks off to get them out to you — at the cheapest possible prices.

Contents

Unit 1 — Developing Scientific Skills

Unit 2 — Science for the Needs of Society

Unit 3 — Science at Work

Published by Coordination Group Publications Ltd.

Editors:
Ellen Bowness, Tom Cain, Gemma Hallam, Sarah Hilton, Andy Park,
Rose Parkin, Kate Redmond, Claire Thompson, Julie Wakeling.

Contributors:
Mike Bossart, James Foster, Andy Rankin, Claire Reed, Philip Rushworth, Adrian Schmit,
Claire Stebbing, Moira Steven, Pat Szczesniak, Mike Thompson, Sophie Watkins.
Including original material by Paddy Gannon.

ISBN-10: 1 84146 613 1
ISBN-13: 978 1 84146 613 2

With thanks to Glenn Rogers for the proofreading.
With thanks to Katie Steele for the copyright research.

With thanks to Science Photo Library for permission to reproduce the photographs used
on pages 3, 58, 108, 110 and 123.

Groovy website: www.cgpbooks.co.uk

Printed by Elanders Hindson Ltd, Newcastle upon Tyne.
Jolly bits of clipart from CorelDRAW®

Avoiding Hazards

Scientific work can be <u>dangerous</u>. You need to be able to work <u>safely</u> in order to <u>prevent</u> accidents from happening. This applies to all workplaces, e.g. school and industrial labs.

There are Six Main Types of Hazard You Should be Aware of

Hazards need to be <u>identified</u> so that they can be <u>avoided</u>.
So, first things first — what types of hazard are there?

Hmm... Where did my bacteria sample go?

1) <u>MICROORGANISMS</u> — these are a particular problem in <u>microbiology labs</u>. The biggest hazard is coming into contact with microorganisms that can <u>cause disease</u>, e.g. <u>viruses</u> and <u>bacteria</u> (see page 57 for more).

2) <u>RADIATION</u> — this is emitted by <u>radioactive materials</u>. The effect on body tissues can be devastating (<u>nausea</u>, <u>weakened immune system</u>, even <u>death</u>) so you need to take precautions. This <u>hazard symbol</u> is used to label a radioactive source.

3) <u>CHEMICALS</u> — There are different types of hazardous chemical, each with a <u>hazard warning symbol</u>:

 <u>Oxidising</u> — These provide <u>oxygen</u>, which allows other materials to <u>burn more fiercely</u>, e.g. liquid oxygen.

 <u>Toxic</u> — Can cause <u>death</u> either by being <u>swallowed</u>, <u>breathed</u> in, or <u>absorbed</u> through the skin, e.g. cyanide.

 <u>Flammable</u> — <u>Catch fire</u> easily, e.g. petrol.

 <u>Corrosive</u> — <u>Attacks and destroys materials</u>, particularly <u>living tissue</u> such as eyes and skin, e.g. sulfuric acid.

 <u>Irritant</u> — Not corrosive but can cause <u>reddening or blistering</u> of the skin, e.g. bleach.

4) <u>ELECTRICITY</u> — electrical hazards include long or frayed cables, cables touching something hot or wet, damaged plugs, overloaded sockets and machines without covers. Electrical hazards can cause <u>electric shocks</u> that may lead to <u>burns</u> or <u>death</u>.

5) <u>GAS</u> — it's important to make sure all gas hoses and taps are in <u>proper working order</u>. Gas is <u>flammable</u>, but thanks to its <u>smell</u> it's usually pretty obvious if someone leaves a tap on. However, left unnoticed it can cause <u>suffocation</u> or an <u>explosion</u>.

6) <u>FIRE</u> — many things in the workplace can cause fires, particularly in the petrochemical industry. <u>Damaged electrical appliances</u> are a big culprit. For more on fire see page 5.

Safety Signs Warn You of Hazards in the Workplace

<u>Safety signs</u> give health and safety information in the normal course of work. There are <u>four colours</u> of safety sign — they have specific meanings.

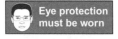 <u>Blue</u> — <u>mandatory</u> sign. Instruction <u>must</u> be followed.

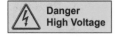 <u>Yellow</u> — <u>warning</u> sign. Take <u>care</u>.

 <u>Green</u> — <u>safety</u> information. E.g. fire exit / first aid point.

 <u>Red</u> — <u>prohibition</u> sign. Action shown must <u>not</u> be carried out.

Risk — not just a thrilling board game...

You'll need this stuff for doing your <u>report</u>, and if you don't follow my advice, then you're just asking for <u>trouble</u>. Don't come crying if you catch <u>hepatitis</u> or <u>electrocute</u> yourself on an overloaded socket.

Avoiding Hazards

Once you've identified your hazards, the next step is to prevent accidents from happening.

The Risk of Injury can be Reduced in Four Ways

The majority of accidents happen because of human error.

The chances of an accident happening are reduced by things like:

1) Proper behaviour — This includes things like not running around the laboratory, and holding scissors or blades in the correct way. It's also important not to eat, drink or smoke in the lab — this is especially important when handling microorganisms and toxic or flammable chemicals.

2) Using equipment properly — all equipment will have instructions and it's important to follow these exactly. Improper use might damage the equipment, but could also lead to serious injury.

3) Using protective and safety equipment — if it's needed, protective equipment has to be provided — it's the law (see below). Lab coats protect your clothes and safety glasses prevent chemicals or flying glass from damaging your eyes. In some scientific workplaces such as hospital laboratories it's important for workers to wear masks and gloves to prevent them being infected with nasty diseases.

4) Following correct procedures — when carrying out an experiment you should always have a well-planned procedure before beginning. It's important to follow the procedures, e.g. using too much of a substance could result in injury if the substance is toxic or flammable.

When carrying out any experiment it's important to have the right protective equipment.

Workplaces are Governed by Health and Safety Regulations

Health and safety legislation is there to provide employees with a safe and healthy working environment. There's a long list of regulations, which cover things like:

1) General health and safety — the workplace must not be a big risk to the people who work there.

2) Electricity — covering the safe use of electricity (obvious really).

3) Personal protective equipment — employers have to provide protective equipment free of charge where it's needed, e.g. goggles, gloves, helmets etc.

4) Control of hazardous substances — employers are required to label all hazardous substances. They must also have a policy on how the risks of using them can be kept as low as possible.

Protective equipment like helmets and safe footwear must be provided.

> Employers are legally required to assess the risks within the workplace. A risk assessment is an examination of what could cause harm in the workplace. There are five stages to a risk assessment:
> 1) Look for hazards.
> 2) Assess who may be harmed and how.
> 3) Decide what action, if any, needs to be taken to reduce the risk.
> 4) Document the findings.
> 5) Review the risk assessment regularly.

Health and safety officials can enter workplaces at any time to carry out an inspection. Where they find problems they can issue instructions for improvements or stop work being carried out altogether. If breaches of health and safety regulations are really serious employers could end up in court.

It's better to be safe than sorry...

All this might seem pretty dull but you'll be thanking your lucky stars when some rather fetching safety glasses save you from losing your eye in a freak beaker accident.

Radioactive Substances

Many industries use radioactive materials, but they can be <u>dangerous</u> because they <u>produce radiation</u>. This can <u>damage</u> your body, so it's pretty important to know how to <u>handle</u> and <u>dispose</u> of these materials in a safe way.

Care <u>Must be Taken When</u> <u>Handling Radioactive Substances</u>

On average, there's one serious incident (resulting in <u>death</u> or <u>serious injury</u>) involving <u>radioactive material</u> in the world each year. The figures are so low because laboratories take <u>precautions</u> when handling radioactive material.

1) <u>Never</u> allow <u>skin contact</u> with a source — always handle with <u>tongs</u>.

2) Keep the source at <u>arm's length</u> to keep it <u>as far</u> from the body <u>as possible</u>.

3) Keep the source <u>pointing away</u> from the body and <u>avoid looking directly at it</u>. (And <u>don't</u> point it at <u>anyone else</u> whilst you're doing this.)

4) <u>Always</u> keep the source in a <u>lead-lined box</u> and put it back in <u>as soon</u> as the experiment is <u>over</u>.

Extra Precautions <u>are Needed for</u> <u>Industrial</u> <u>Workers</u>

1) Radioactive substances are used widely in <u>industry</u> — <u>hospitals</u> use them for things like <u>radiotherapy</u> and <u>diagnostic imaging</u>. They're also used for <u>sterilising food</u> and in <u>nuclear power stations</u>.

2) In hospitals workers like <u>radiographers</u> have to keep their <u>radiation exposure</u> to a <u>minimum</u>.
   - They <u>leave the room</u> or stand behind a <u>protective screen</u> when doing things like carrying out radiotherapy (which uses a type of radiation).

3) Some <u>nuclear power station workers</u> also have to take extra precautions:
   - To prevent workers being exposed to radiation <u>lead-lined suits</u>, <u>lead or concrete barriers</u> and <u>thick lead screens</u> are often used.
   - Some workers have to wear <u>full protective suits</u> to prevent <u>radioactive particles</u> from being <u>inhaled</u> or getting trapped <u>under their fingernails</u> etc.
   - Working in highly radioactive areas is often <u>too dangerous</u> for people so workers use <u>remote-controlled robot arms</u> to move things about. Cool.

STEVE ALLEN / SCIENCE PHOTO LIBRARY

Radioactive Material <u>Used in Schools Produces</u> <u>Low-Level Waste</u>

1) The majority of radioactive waste produced by hospitals, universities, schools and colleges is <u>very low-level waste</u>. It usually includes things like gloves, masks, bench coverings, paper towels etc. (Nuclear power stations produce <u>high-level</u> radioactive waste, which has to be dealt with in a special way — see page 93.)

2) Very low-level waste can be sealed in a <u>strong plastic bag</u>, then <u>thrown away</u>. It <u>is</u> safe to dispose of this waste in landfill sites because the level of radiation is so <u>low</u>.

3) Disposal of radioactive <u>sources</u> (the material that's actually used for experiments) is slightly different. Solid sources (like the ones you'll use at school) should be put in a <u>small container</u> and filled up with <u>plaster of Paris</u>. The container <u>should not</u> be labelled to show that it contains a radioactive source (if you labelled it some nosey parker might pick it up). The container can then be put in with normal rubbish (but you can't dispose of sources this way more than once a week).

Robot arms — my preferred dancing style...

It might sound a bit careless just to put radioactive waste out for the bin men but it's only <u>very</u> low-level waste. <u>Nuclear power plants</u> have to be extra <u>careful</u> with their waste. They can't just go around putting weapons grade plutonium in plastic bags and chucking them in the bin — that'd just be wrong.

First Aid

Now, if you've been paying attention over the last few pages then hopefully you'll never need to use what you learn on this page. Having said that, there's always going to be some idiot clowning around, causing trouble for the rest of us — so it's probably for the best if you have a good read over this stuff anyway.

First Aiders Could be the Difference Between Life and Death

It's a good idea, but not a legal requirement, to have as many people as possible trained in basic first aid. They could be vital in saving the life of a person in any situation, e.g. at work, in the street or at home.

Training courses in basic first aid are provided by St. John Ambulance, St. Andrew's Ambulance Association, and the British Red Cross. All these organisations have websites and can be found in the phone book.

In Any First Aid Situation Follow a Clear Plan of Action

This will stop you placing yourself in danger and will help you to respond in the right way:

1) Assess the situation — what has happened? Is anyone still in danger?

2) Make the area safe — protect yourself and the casualty from danger.

3) Give emergency aid — give appropriate first aid (see below). If there's more than one casualty, the ones with life-threatening conditions should be treated first.

4) Get help — once the casualty has been stabilised call an ambulance.

You Need to Know the Treatment for Common Injuries

There are seven common injuries that you might encounter in the laboratory. You need to know what they are, what basic first aid should be given and when it would be unsafe to give first aid.

1) Heat burns and scalds — if they're minor flood the injured part with cool water for at least 10 minutes, then cover with a sterile dressing. If they're pretty serious cool, damp cloths should be used instead and you should ring an ambulance.

2) Chemical burns — flood the injured part with water for at least 20 minutes, remove any contaminated clothing and arrange for the casualty to be sent to hospital. You should not attempt to give first aid if there are chemical fumes present or if there has been significant chemical spillage.

3) Poisoning due to fume inhalation — the priority is to get the casualty into fresh air and to get medical help. You should not attempt to move the casualty if there are fumes in the area.

4) Poisoning due to swallowing — the casualty needs to go straight to hospital. Never attempt to make the casualty vomit and never give them anything to drink (although small sips of water are OK if they've swallowed something corrosive).

5) Electric shock — turn off the electrical supply before doing anything else (don't touch the victim until you've done this), then ring an ambulance. If the casualty stops breathing you need to be prepared to give rescue breathing (mouth-to-mouth resuscitation) and chest compressions.

6) Cuts — clean the wound under running water, raise the injured part if possible and apply a dressing (don't try to pull objects out of wounds — pad around them and bandage over the top, then send the casualty to hospital).

7) Particles or chemicals in the eye — particles or chemicals should be flushed out of the eye using lots of sterile water. You need to do this for 10 minutes, then bandage the eye before sending the casualty to hospital.

First aid — relief for someone in need of a brew...

An important thing to remember about first aid is that you shouldn't do anything that might put you or the casualty at risk. Never do anything that you're not sure about just for the sake of doing something.

Fire Prevention

Fires are responsible for many deaths every year, but only 6% of these occur in the workplace. The low figure is all thanks to things like fire instructions, sprinklers and extinguishers...

Fire Instructions Tell You What To Do in the Event of a Fire

Fire instruction notices should be displayed at prominent points in a building — they tell you the quickest route to leave the building and where to assemble. Make sure you're familiar with your school lab ones. Also make sure you know what the fire alarm sounds like — it should be tested at least once a week.

If the fire alarm sounds you should:

1) Leave the building by the quickest escape route — never use lifts, escalators or revolving doors.
2) Go to the designated assembly point and wait there until a fire warden takes a roll-call — don't wander off or go home, or somebody might re-enter a burning building to look for you.

If you discover a fire you should:

1) Sound the fire alarm (usually by smashing the glass at a fire alarm point).
2) Call the fire brigade (though some alarms will automatically alert the fire brigade).
3) If the fire is small enough, use a hand-held extinguisher to tackle it (the different types of extinguisher are listed below) — but never put yourself at risk in attempting to put a fire out, and always stand between the fire and your escape route.
4) Leave the building by the quickest escape route and report to the assembly area.

Fire Doors and Sprinkler Systems can Stop Fire Spreading

Fires can spread easily through open areas such as corridors and stairwells. There are two common features installed in the workplace to slow down the spread of fire.

1) Fire doors act as barriers to hold back smoke and flames. Fire doors must be kept shut at all times or be fitted with automatic closing devices — never wedge a fire door open.
2) Sprinkler systems are usually installed in high-risk areas, such as storerooms. They're very effective at containing fires — they spray water from the ceilings. But, they're expensive to install and maintain, they need a water supply at high pressure, and if there's a minor fire (which can be put out with a fire extinguisher) they can cause a lot of unnecessary mess and damage to equipment and stock.

Know Which Type of Fire Extinguisher to Use

There are six types of hand-held fire extinguisher. All new fire extinguishers are painted red with a colour-coded band or panel to identify its contents and the type of fire it can be used on. It's important to use the right fire extinguisher for the type of fire — you could make the fire worse if you use the wrong one.

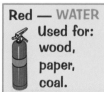
Red — WATER
Used for:
wood,
paper,
coal.

Black — CARBON DIOXIDE
Used for:
wood, paper,
coal, liquids,
electrical equipment.

Green — VAPORISING LIQUID
Used for:
liquids,
electrical equipment.

You can also use a fire blanket to smother a fire if it's small and self-contained.

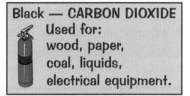
Cream — FOAM
Used for:
wood,
paper,
coal, liquids.

Blue — DRY POWDER
Used for:
wood, paper, coal,
liquids, gases,
electrical equipment.

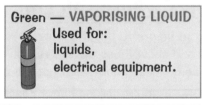
Yellow — WET CHEMICAL
Used for:
cooking oil
and fats.

Fire doors — bet they have hot handles...

Remember — it's dead important to use the right kind of extinguisher for a fire. You should never use water on an oil fire (e.g. a chip pan fire) — it could make the fire even worse and cause an explosion.

Report: Developing Scientific Skills 1

Now on to the unpleasant subject of <u>assessment</u> — those lovely examiners want you to write a report on working safely in the workplace.

You Need to Write a Report on Working Safely

This will make up the FIRST part of your portfolio for
<u>UNIT 1: DEVELOPING SCIENTIFIC SKILLS</u>.

Your report will have <u>three bits</u> to it:
1) Information about <u>HAZARDS and RISKS</u> in the <u>workplace</u>.
2) Information about <u>FIRST AID</u> in the workplace.
3) Information about <u>FIRE PREVENTION</u> in the workplace.

You Can Make a Leaflet or Presentation Instead of a Report

You <u>don't</u> have to <u>write a report</u> if you don't want to (but you have to write <u>something</u>)
— you could put the same information in a <u>leaflet</u> or a <u>presentation</u>.

- <u>Leaflet</u> — make sure it <u>looks like</u> a real leaflet. Use a <u>logical layout</u> (with subheadings) and check that when it's <u>folded</u> you can <u>still read everything</u>.

- <u>Presentation</u> — make sure it's <u>clear</u> and <u>easy to follow</u> (don't get carried away with fancy special effects). Keep it <u>short</u> (no more than 15 minutes) and <u>don't waffle</u>.

You Need to Research These Topics

You need to use a <u>wide range</u> of <u>sources</u> when you're putting your report together. It's no good just using this revision guide. There are plenty of things you can use:

- <u>Websites</u> — e.g. the <u>St. John Ambulance</u> website (www.sja.org.uk) or <u>general resource websites</u> about science (e.g. www.psigate.ac.uk).

- <u>Leaflets</u> — e.g. the <u>Fire Service</u> publishes leaflets on general fire safety and the <u>Health and Safety Executive</u> publish free leaflets on health and safety.

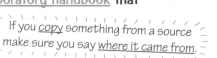

- <u>Books</u> — e.g. your <u>school</u> or <u>library</u> might have a <u>laboratory handbook</u> that includes loads of health and safety information.

If you <u>copy</u> something from a source make sure you say <u>where it came from</u>.

Use Examples Where You Can

Your report's going to be pretty <u>dull</u> if it's just a list of hazards, first aid and fire prevention measures. To spice it up a bit and show those examiners you've <u>done your research</u> you can include some <u>relevant examples</u>. Here's some ideas about what you could include:

- <u>Photographs</u> — if you're talking about hazard signs or safety signs you could take a photo of some in your school lab and stick them in to illustrate your point.

- <u>Diagrams</u> — if you're talking about the fire procedures for your laboratory you could draw a diagram of the exit route you should take if the fire alarm sounds.

- <u>Case studies</u> — you can include case studies to illustrate various things, e.g. what happens if you use the wrong type of fire extinguisher.

Reports, investigations? Who do you think you are? — Poirot?

There's no magic number of words that your report/leaflet/presentation must be — it has to be long enough to get your <u>point across clearly</u>, but not so long that you fill it with <u>waffle</u>. Good luck.

Following Standard Procedures

This section is all about how scientists work when they carry out <u>practical tasks</u>, how they <u>record results</u>, how they <u>interpret results</u>, basically how they <u>carry out their jobs</u>. But first things first, they have to be able to follow a <u>procedure</u>. Whether making acids or measuring giraffes, scientists follow '<u>standard procedures</u>' — clear instructions describing exactly how to carry out these practical tasks.

Standard Procedures <u>Mean</u> Everyone <u>Does Things the</u> Same Way

Standard procedures are <u>agreed methods of working</u> — they are chosen because they're the <u>safest</u>, <u>most effective</u> and <u>accurate methods</u> to use. Standard procedures can be agreed within a company, nationally, or internationally.

Standard procedures are used for a wide range of things, e.g.
1) <u>Taking measurements</u> (e.g. measuring the density of boats).
2) <u>Preparing and purifying compounds</u> (e.g. making medicines).
3) <u>Monitoring changes</u> (e.g. monitoring water quality).

<u>There are</u> Seven Steps <u>to Following a</u> Standard Procedure

When following a standard procedure, you need to:
1) <u>Read the procedure</u> and check you <u>understand</u> everything.

2) Complete a <u>health and safety</u> check of your <u>working area</u>.

3) Complete a <u>risk assessment</u> for the activity.

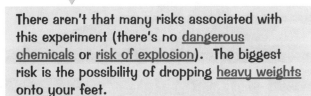

There aren't that many risks associated with this experiment (there's no <u>dangerous chemicals</u> or <u>risk of explosion</u>). The biggest risk is the possibility of dropping <u>heavy weights</u> onto your feet.

4) <u>Collect the equipment and materials</u> you need, and set out your working area.

5) Follow the instructions <u>one step at a time</u>.

6) Select instruments that give <u>appropriate precision</u>, and use them to make <u>accurate observations</u> or <u>measurements</u>.

7) Identify possible sources of <u>error</u> and <u>repeat observations</u> and <u>measurements</u> where necessary to improve <u>reliability</u>.

Densicorp Standard Procedure for Measuring the Density of Materials:
1) Ensure test specimens have a regular shape (e.g. cubes or cylinders).
2) Measure the specimen's mass to the nearest 0.01 g.
3) Measure the specimen's dimensions to the nearest mm.
4) Calculate the volume of the specimen.
5) Calculate the density of the specimen using the formula: density = mass ÷ volume.

You'll need a <u>top pan balance</u>, a <u>ruler</u> and some <u>materials</u> to measure.

Your balance will need to be able to <u>accurately</u> measure to the <u>nearest 0.01 g</u>, and your ruler to the <u>nearest mm</u>.

Before packing away all your equipment have a look over your <u>results</u> — if any look <u>out of place</u> repeat the experiment and have a <u>think</u> about why they might have been <u>wrong</u>.

<u>Tamoto techkup — a sauce of error...</u>
There are so many reasons why you should follow <u>standard procedures</u>. They're <u>tried and tested</u>, so you're more likely to get <u>good results</u> and less likely to <u>injure yourself</u>. They should have them for everything, like getting dressed — there's more 'trouser-related accidents' every year than you'd think.

Handling Scientific Equipment

When carrying out <u>any experiment</u>, one of the most <u>important</u> things is using the <u>right equipment</u> for the job at hand. You wouldn't get very far if you tried boiling water in a china tea cup using a cigarette lighter, and testing the temperature of the water with your fingers — trust me, I've been there.

<u>Standard</u> <u>Lab Equipment — Know Your Stuff</u>

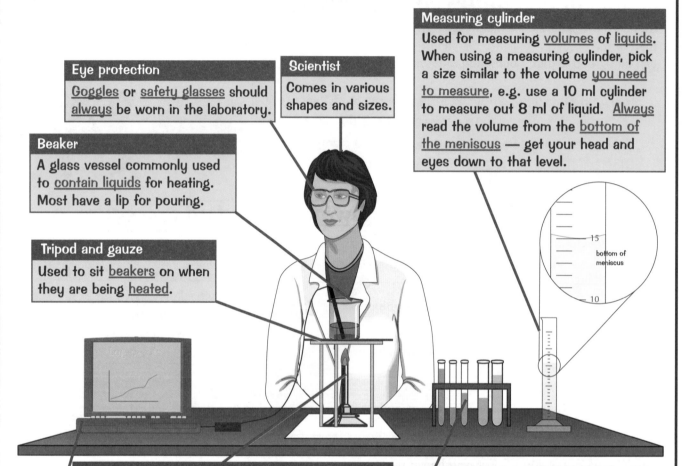

Measuring cylinder

Used for measuring <u>volumes</u> of <u>liquids</u>. When using a measuring cylinder, pick a size similar to the volume <u>you need to measure</u>, e.g. use a 10 ml cylinder to measure out 8 ml of liquid. <u>Always</u> read the volume from the <u>bottom of the meniscus</u> — get your head and eyes down to that level.

Eye protection

<u>Goggles</u> or <u>safety glasses</u> should <u>always</u> be worn in the laboratory.

Scientist

Comes in various shapes and sizes.

Beaker

A glass vessel commonly used to <u>contain liquids</u> for heating. Most have a lip for pouring.

Tripod and gauze

Used to sit <u>beakers</u> on when they are being <u>heated</u>.

bottom of meniscus

Bunsen burner

Used to <u>heat</u> substances in the laboratory. They have an <u>air hole</u> at the bottom which can be <u>opened</u> and <u>closed</u>. When the valve is fully closed the flame burns <u>orange</u> (this is known as the <u>safety flame</u>), but when closed the flame is <u>blue</u>. The Bunsen should always be lit with the air hole <u>open</u>. And remember — always use a <u>heatproof mat</u>.

Test tube rack, test tubes and boiling tubes

<u>Test tubes</u> are long thin glass tubes with a U-shaped bottom. They are used to hold <u>small</u> amounts for heating, though <u>boiling tubes</u> (larger versions of test tubes) are usually favoured for <u>heating liquids</u>.

Data logger

Data loggers <u>accurately</u> record changes in things like <u>temperature</u>, <u>pH</u> and <u>salinity</u> over time. You need to be able to <u>set up</u> a data logger (which may involve attaching different probes), <u>transfer</u> the data to a computer and be able to <u>calibrate</u> it. E.g. to calibrate a temperature probe, dip it into <u>freezing water</u> and then into <u>boiling water</u>. To calibrate pH or salinity, data loggers are usually supplied with a set of <u>standard solutions</u> with known values.

<u>Beaker, Bunsen — we're just missing Kermit and Fozzie Bear...</u>

It's all very well knowing how to use this gear, but you've also got to be able to use it <u>safely</u>. Remember the basics, like not <u>eating</u> or <u>running</u> and generally not acting like an <u>idiot</u> in the lab — if your memory needs refreshing have a look back over Section 1.1 (pages 1-6).

Handling Scientific Equipment

In <u>microbiology</u>, everything is pretty <u>small</u> (the clue's in the name). A lot of the equipment you'll need to use for microbiology makes <u>handling</u> and <u>seeing</u> small things a lot <u>easier</u>.

Equipment for Microbiology

Microscope
Used to view <u>microorganisms</u> and other things which are <u>too small</u> to view with the <u>naked eye</u>.

Mounted needle
Used to <u>prepare</u> glass slides to avoid getting grubby <u>fingerprints</u> all over them.

Glass slides and cover slips
<u>Before</u> samples can be <u>viewed</u> they need to be placed onto a <u>glass slide</u>. A <u>cover slip</u> is then placed on top to <u>hold the sample</u> in place.

Sample bottles
Bottles to put samples in.

Pipette
Used to add <u>small</u> volumes of a liquid, <u>drop by drop</u>.

Petri dish
Shallow plastic or glass dish used to grow microorganisms in. They're filled with a <u>gel</u> (called <u>agar</u>), which contains the <u>nutrients</u> needed for microorganisms to grow.

Stain
To make some samples <u>easier to view</u> they are <u>stained</u>. A common stain used in the lab is <u>methylene blue</u>.

Inoculating loop
Used to transfer samples, e.g. bacteria, onto agar plates.

Assay discs
Small circles of filter paper which are <u>soaked</u> in <u>different chemicals</u> and then placed on top the agar. This is done to investigate the <u>effect</u> of different chemicals on <u>microorganisms</u>.

Incubator
When microorganisms are <u>cultured</u> (grown) they must be kept at a <u>certain temperature</u>. Incubators are used to keep them at this temperature. (<u>Water baths</u> can sometimes also be used).

Autoclave
Once the experiment has finished the microorganisms must be <u>disposed of safely</u>. An autoclave is like a large, very hot <u>pressure cooker</u> that <u>kills</u> the microorganisms using <u>high temperatures</u>.

Assay old chap, what a ruddy good page. Brandy anyone...

One of the most important things when handling microorganisms is to use <u>aseptic techniques</u> — these stop you spreading nasty microorganisms everywhere. There's more on aseptic techniques on p.13.

Handling Scientific Equipment

<u>Microscopes</u> and <u>Petri dishes</u> wouldn't be much use for <u>flame tests</u>, so there's even more <u>specialised</u> <u>equipment</u> needed for <u>chemical analysis</u>.

Equipment for Chemical Analysis

Burette

Used to dispense a <u>measured volume</u> of liquid. Their most common use is in <u>titrations</u> (see p.120). As with <u>measuring cylinders</u> (see p.8) you need to read the volume from the <u>bottom of the meniscus</u>. You should fill pipettes and burettes to about 3 cm <u>above</u> the desired amount, then carefully drop the level down to what you need. It's also important to clamp the burette properly so that it doesn't fall over and smash.

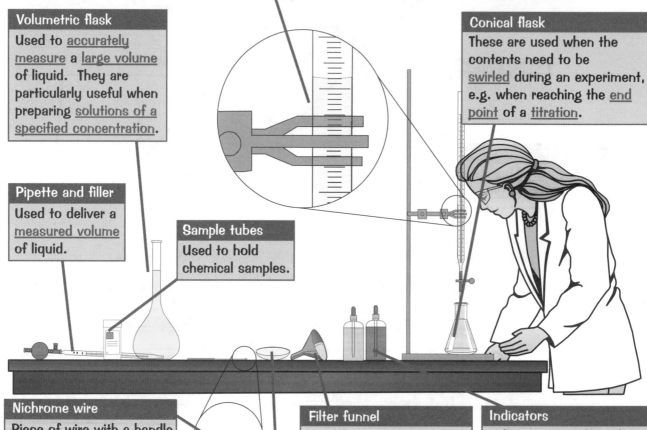

Volumetric flask

Used to <u>accurately</u> <u>measure</u> a <u>large volume</u> of liquid. They are particularly useful when preparing <u>solutions of a</u> <u>specified concentration</u>.

Conical flask

These are used when the contents need to be <u>swirled</u> during an experiment, e.g. when reaching the <u>end</u> <u>point</u> of a <u>titration</u>.

Pipette and filler

Used to deliver a <u>measured volume</u> of liquid.

Sample tubes

Used to hold chemical samples.

Nichrome wire

Piece of wire with a handle at one end and a small <u>loop</u> at the other. Usually used in <u>flame tests</u>.

Watch glass

A circular piece of glassware shaped like a <u>small bowl</u>. It's used in experiments to view an <u>evaporating liquid</u>.

Filter funnel

Used for <u>separating</u> solids from liquids (with <u>filter paper</u> folded up and placed inside the funnel). Also useful for filling things with a <u>narrow</u> <u>neck</u> (e.g. <u>burettes</u> and <u>volumetric flasks</u>).

Indicators

Indicators provide a clear <u>colour change</u> when a reaction takes place. E.g. they're used for determining the <u>end point</u> of a <u>titration</u>.

Top pan balance

Used to weigh out amounts of a substance. They can measure with an extremely high degree of <u>precision</u>. It's important to 'zero' the balance <u>before</u> use (press the T (tare) button when there's nothing on it). Balances need to be <u>calibrated</u> (they usually come with a set of <u>weights</u> of <u>known mass</u>).

Pipettes — aren't they a girl band from Brighton...

The same old <u>safety rules</u> apply, but be careful — analytical chemistry uses loads of <u>hazardous chemicals</u>.

Handling Scientific Equipment

Like all good things in life, this small section on scientific equipment must come to an end. But wipe away those tears — this page on equipment for materials testing is going to be a right hoot. And as if that wasn't enough, the next few pages are all about investigating living organisms — yay.

Equipment for Materials Testing

Clamp and stand
Large metal stand with a clamp. The clamp can be moved up and down the stand. In materials testing clamps and stands are mostly used for hanging things off to test their strength or elasticity.

Material to be tested
This could be anything. You may need to determine the conductivity of a piece of metal, or the strength of a piece of wire.

Mass hanger and masses
Used for testing the strength of materials. There are different sized masses depending on what you're testing. It's important to pick the right mass for the material you're testing, e.g. it'd be daft to test the strength of cotton thread with a 1 kg mass.

Displacement can
Displacement cans are filled up to just below the arm. The material to be tested is then placed into the can. The amount of water it displaces can be collected and measured.

Power pack
Allows the user to change the voltage of the mains supply to suit the needs of the experiment.

Voltmeter
Used to measure the voltage across a component. Remember, voltmeters must always be connected in parallel.

Ammeter
Measures the current flowing through a circuit. Ammeters should always be connected in series.

Wires and electrodes
These are used to connect everything together and make the test circuit complete.

Components
Materials scientists also use a range of components including fixed capacity and variable resistors, filament lamps, light-emitting diodes and thermistors.

Clamp... tweezers... stat...

Well, after all of that you should be pretty familiar with the standard equipment used by scientists every day. The more you use equipment like this, the more accurate your experiments will become. You'll also become better at using less familiar equipment. It's a bit like riding a bike — the more you ride a bike, the better you get and the better you'll be at riding something less familiar, like a horse. OK, so it's not really like riding a bike, but people should ride bikes more often.

Investigating Living Organisms

Microbiologists use microscopes to study things that are too small to see with the naked eye. This can include really, really small organisms (like bacteria) or the cells and tissues that make up larger organisms.

Ten Easy Steps to Setting Up a Light Microscope

1) Always carry your microscope by the handle.
2) If it has a built-in light, plug it in and switch it on.
3) If your microscope has a mirror, place it near a lamp or a window, and angle the mirror so light shines up through the hole in the stage.

> Don't reflect direct sunlight into the microscope — it could damage your eyes.

4) Place a slide on the stage, and clip it in position.
5) Select the lowest powered objective lens.
6) Before looking down the microscope, position the objective lens just above the slide (do this by turning the focusing knob, which raises and lowers either the objective lens or the stage).
7) Look down the eyepiece, and carefully start to focus by turning the focusing knob.
8) Focus until you get a clear image.
9) If you need to look at the slide with greater magnification, switch to a higher powered objective lens (a longer one). With some microscopes you can also swap the eyepiece lens.
10) Refocus the microscope (repeat steps 7 and 8).

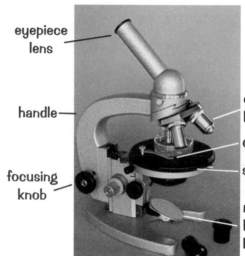

eyepiece lens
objective lens
handle
clip
stage
focusing knob
mirror or built-in light

> Always turn the focusing knob so that the objective lens is moving away from the slide — this is so the lens and slide don't crash together. Some microscopes have a coarse focusing knob and a fine focusing knob. Use the coarse knob to make large adjustments, and the fine knob to make smaller ones.

Samples Need to be Prepared Before Investigation

You can't just slap a piece of tissue underneath a microscope — it has to be on a slide.

1) Use a pipette to put one drop of mountant (a clear, gloopy liquid) in the middle of the slide — this secures the sample in place. Sometimes water can be used.
2) Use forceps to place your sample on the slide (e.g. a hair for forensic examination).
3) Make sure the mountant is holding the sample in place, and it's positioned so it will all be under the cover slip.
4) Sometimes a drop of stain (e.g. methylene blue) is added to make the samples easier to see under a microscope.
5) Place the cover slip at one end of the sample, holding it at an angle with a mounted needle.
6) Carefully lower the cover slip onto the slide. Press it down gently with the needle so that no air bubbles are trapped under it.

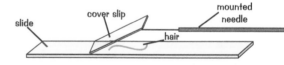

cover slip
mounted needle
slide
hair

> Always handle slides and cover slips by their edges to avoid finger marks.

Cover, slip — I thought this was science, not cricket...

Nobody knows exactly who invented microscopes or when they were invented, but it's thought to have been some time in the 16th century — lots of people claim to have invented them (including my uncle Charlie, but he's slightly crazy). These days we've got some pretty cool microscopes, e.g. electron microscopes — these produce 3D images and have magnifications beyond your wildest dreams.

Investigating Living Organisms

In their investigations, microbiologists aim to get the best results possible and to stay out of harm's way whilst they're doing it — they achieve this using aseptic techniques.

Microorganisms are Everywhere

Microorganisms are everywhere — in the air, on our hands, on laboratory benches and in hospitals. There are useful microorganisms, like the ones that make bread, beer, yoghurt and antibiotics (see pages 32-33). There are also harmful microorganisms — ones that can make us ill.

Microbiologists often isolate and grow colonies of microorganisms for investigation. Culturing (growing) microorganisms can be dangerous, so scientists need to:

1) Make sure they don't contaminate the laboratory with the microorganisms they culture.
2) Make sure their work doesn't become contaminated with microorganisms from the environment.

Aseptic Techniques Prevent Contamination

Aseptic techniques are standard procedures used by microbiologists to prevent contamination. The techniques involve creating a clean, contained environment to culture microorganisms in.

1) Sterilise all equipment before and after use.
2) Keep samples containing microorganisms in sample bottles with lids.
3) When opening a sample bottle to use it, close it again as soon as possible.
4) Pass the tops of sample bottles through a Bunsen flame whenever lids are removed.
5) Don't put lids down on benches — hold them with your little finger or your other hand.
6) Don't open Petri dishes until you are ready to use them.
7) Don't put any equipment that comes into contact with microorganisms down on benches.
8) Seal agar plates with sticky tape.
9) Before the plates are incubated, label them with your name, the date and what you've put on the plate.
10) Don't open agar plates once they have been sealed.
11) Dispose of cultures safely — usually done by pressure sterilising in an autoclave.

In large commercial laboratories they employ chickens to sit on plates and incubate them.

Microorganisms Can be Used to Make Yoghurt

Some microorganisms help produce useful products, e.g. beer, wine, bread and a whole host of dairy products are all made using microorganisms. Ever fancied making your own yoghurt — then read on.

1) Pour 250 cm³ of UHT milk into a sterile beaker.
2) Place the beaker in a water bath at 37 °C and stir gently until the milk reaches the same temperature.

The microorganisms that make yoghurt will die if they get too hot, and they won't grow very fast if they're too cold.

3) Add some 'yoghurt starter culture' and stir — you can buy special starter cultures, or just use a tablespoon of ordinary live yoghurt.
4) Cover the beaker with foil and leave it in the water bath for 24 hours.
5) Place the beaker in a bowl of cold water and stir until smooth.
6) Put the beaker in the fridge for a few hours for the yogurt to thicken.

Working with sewage requires a septic technique...

It's a bit dull and some of it's just common sense, but it's still important. Scientists in industry need to use aseptic techniques all the time — and they're crucial in hospitals.

Investigating Living Organisms

It's not just making yoghurt that requires a cleanly approach though — aseptic techniques are always used when dealing with microorganisms and even when making plant clones.

Antimicrobial Agents Inhibit the Growth of Microorganisms

Antimicrobial agents (like antiseptics, disinfectants and antibiotics) kill or prevent the growth of microorganisms. You can compare the effectiveness of different antimicrobial agents:

1) Use a pipette to put five drops of bacterial culture into a Petri dish.

2) Pour 20 cm³ of molten agar into the Petri dish and replace the lid.

3) Mix the contents by sliding the dish gently over the bench.

4) Leave the plate to set.

5) Mark out four quadrants on the base of the dish, and label them A-D.

6) Using forceps, dip a 5 mm assay disc into distilled water and place the disc on the surface of the agar, in the middle of quadrant D — this is the control.

7) Dip three assay discs into three different antiseptics and add them to the other quadrants — remember to note which antiseptic went in which quadrant.

8) Tape down the lid, and incubate the dish at 25 °C for 48 hours.

9) Measure the zone of inhibition around each disc — you could stand the dish on graph paper and count the squares beneath each zone, or just measure the diameter and calculate the area of the circle).

Inhibition zone

Assay disc

The zone of inhibition is the clear area around an assay disc where no microbes have grown. The larger the inhibition zone, the more effective the antimicrobial agent.

Plants are Cloned Using Aseptic Techniques

Plants are cloned in the lab using aseptic techniques. Cloning means producing offspring which are genetically the same as their parent. When making clones, it's best to start them growing in aseptic conditions — this prevents bacteria or fungi from growing.

Here's how you do it:

1) Wash some seeds in bleach solution, to make their surfaces sterile.

2) Leave the washed seeds to germinate in sterile water, in a sterile container. When seedlings have grown, you can clone each one.

3) Cut small pieces from the root — these bits are called cuttings.

4) Put your cuttings in a Petri dish filled with nutrient agar. The agar needs to contain sugar and other nutrients which the cuttings need to survive until they're bigger. (Make sure everything is sterile, or microorganisms will grow.)

5) Seal the dishes to keep them sterile (and also to stop the cuttings losing too much water).

6) Leave them in a warm dark place for several days. Once the cuttings have grown into little plants, they can be planted out as normal.

Try doing this with mustard seeds.

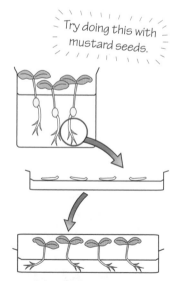

Aunty Microbial — she's married to uncle Bob...

Zones of inhibition, agents killing stuff — this sounds more like a page from a book written by a former member of the SAS than how to develop your scientific skills. I'd love to tell you more secrets about plant cloning, but I'd have to kill you. On that note, I think it's time for some chemistry.

Analytical Chemistry

Chemical analysis is important in environmental science. Say lots of fish in a river die suddenly and it's suspected that pollution from a nearby factory is to blame — an analytical chemist could find out exactly what's in the water. Forensic scientists also use chemical analysis, e.g. to detect banned substances in blood or urine samples from athletes or to identify substances present at a crime scene.

Qualitative and Quantitative Analysis

There are two types of chemical analysis:

1) Qualitative analysis tells you what substances are present — this page to page 18.
2) Quantitative analysis tells you how much of a substance is present — see p.19-21.

You Can Identify a Compound by the Ions It Contains

One way to identify a compound is to identify its ions (remember, an ion is just an atom that's gained or lost some electrons — see p.82). E.g. if you know a substance has sodium ions and chloride ions in it (and nothing else) you know it's sodium chloride. The two tests that follow are for metal ions.

See Section 2.4 for more on compounds, atoms, ions and chemical formulas.

Add Sodium Hydroxide and Look for a Coloured Precipitate

1) Many metal hydroxides are insoluble — so they precipitate out of solution when formed.
2) Some of these hydroxide precipitates have a characteristic colour.
3) In this test you just add a few drops of sodium hydroxide solution to a solution of your mystery compound, and see what happens.
4) If a precipitate forms, its colour tells you which metal hydroxide you've made — and so what the metal bit of your mystery compound could be...

Metal ion	Colour of precipitate
Calcium, Ca^{2+}	White
Copper(II), Cu^{2+}	Blue
Iron(II), Fe^{2+}	Sludgy green
Lead, Pb^{2+}	White at first. But if you add loads more sodium hydroxide it forms a colourless solution.

Do a Flame Test

Some metal ions produce pretty flames when they burn — the colour of the flame can tell you which metal is present. This is what you do:

1) Prepare a powdered sample of the mystery substance.
2) Get a wire loop and clean it — by dipping it in some hydrochloric acid.
3) Dip the loop into the sample, then hold the end in a blue Bunsen flame.

Metal ion	Colour of flame
Sodium, Na^+	Yellowy orange
Potassium, K^+	Lilac
Calcium, Ca^{2+}	Brick red
Copper(II), Cu^{2+}	Blue-green
Lead, Pb^{2+}	Blue

One Test isn't Always Enough...

Watch out — sometimes different metal ions give the same result. For example:

- Aluminium behaves like lead when it reacts with sodium hydroxide. So if you only do the sodium hydroxide test, you won't know which it is.
- To be sure, you have to do a flame test as well (lead burns blue, while aluminium doesn't burn with a characteristic colour).

Coloured Precipitate — Purple Rain... (ask your Mum or Dad)

Knowing about all those pretty colours in the flame tests isn't just important for forensic scientists and GCSE Applied Science students — it's also vital for firework-makers. So remember, remember....

Analytical Chemistry

So, imagine you've got a mystery compound and you've already figured out it contains <u>copper</u> ions (using a flame test). You still have to find out whether it's copper <u>carbonate</u>, copper <u>sulfate</u> or what. Luckily, there are more useful tests you can do.

Testing for Carbonates — Use Dilute Acid

<u>Carbonates</u> give off <u>carbon dioxide</u> when added to <u>dilute acids</u>. Here's the method:

1) Put your mystery compound in dilute acid, e.g. <u>dilute hydrochloric acid</u>, and <u>collect</u> any <u>gas</u> given off.

2) Bubble the gas through <u>limewater</u>. If the limewater turns <u>milky</u>, the gas given off is <u>carbon dioxide</u>...

3) ...so your compound contains <u>carbonate</u> ions — CO_3^{2-}.

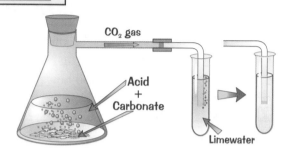

Testing for Sulfates — Hydrochloric Acid then Barium Chloride

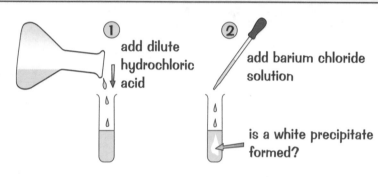

add dilute hydrochloric acid

add barium chloride solution

is a white precipitate formed?

1) Add some <u>dilute hydrochloric acid</u> to a solution of your compound.

2) Then add a few drops of <u>barium chloride solution</u> to the liquid.

3) If you see a <u>white precipitate</u>, there are <u>sulfate</u> ions (SO_4^{2-}) in your compound.

Testing for Chlorides — Nitric Acid then Silver Nitrate

1) Add <u>dilute nitric acid</u> to a solution of your compound.

2) Then add a few drops of <u>silver nitrate solution</u> to the liquid.

3) If you see a <u>white precipitate</u>, there are <u>chloride</u> ions (Cl^-) in your compound.

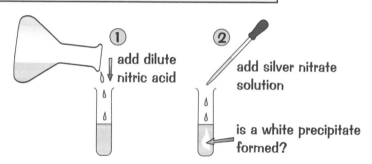

add dilute nitric acid

add silver nitrate solution

is a white precipitate formed?

Drawing Conclusions

The tests above can occasionally be misleading, e.g.:

1) If the <u>carbonate test</u> is positive, it's possible your sample contains hydrogencarbonate ions (HCO_3^-) rather than carbonate ions (CO_3^{2-}).

2) If the <u>sulfate test</u> is positive, your sample might contain hydrogensulfate ions (HSO_4^-) rather than sulfate ions (SO_4^{2-}).

3) The <u>chloride</u> test <u>only</u> works for chloride ions. Hurrah. But... bromide ions (Br^-) produce a <u>cream precipitate</u> that looks quite similar.

Snow White Precipitate — and the Seven Analytical Chemists...

So that's <u>qualitative analysis</u> — finding out what ions you've got and therefore which compound you've got. It's all good clean fun. At least you don't have to <u>memorise</u> what to add to what, and which colours mean which ions. On the next three pages the fun continues with <u>quantitative analysis</u>.

Analytical Chemistry

Many of the tests analytical chemists carry out have <u>practical uses</u> in everyday life — like testing <u>contaminated food</u> and catching people who've been <u>driving</u> after having too much to <u>drink</u>. In addition to <u>chemical tests</u>, they also use <u>spectroscopic techniques</u>.

Compounds Can be Identified Using Spectroscopy

<u>Infrared spectroscopy</u> is another method for identifying the <u>substances</u> present in a <u>sample</u>.

1) Every compound absorbs a <u>unique</u> amount of each frequency of <u>infrared radiation</u> (a type of <u>electromagnetic wave</u> — see pages 108-110 for more on IR and the <u>electromagnetic spectrum</u>).

2) The <u>amount</u> of radiation a compound absorbs is measured using an <u>infrared spectrometer</u> and an **IR** <u>spectrum</u> is produced.

3) The IR spectrum is a bit like a <u>fingerprint</u> for that compound. The spectrum of an <u>unknown compound</u> can be <u>compared</u> to the spectra of known compounds to allow <u>identification</u>. Here's an example:

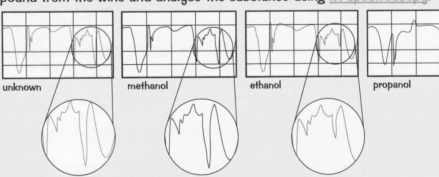

The police are investigating reports that a shipment of wine may be <u>contaminated</u>. Scientists isolate a compound from the wine and analyse the substance using <u>IR spectroscopy</u>.

A forensic scientist compares the IR spectrum of the <u>unknown</u> sample with the IR spectra of three <u>known</u> compounds: <u>methanol</u>, <u>ethanol</u> and <u>propanol</u>.

unknown   methanol   ethanol   propanol

If two spectrum patterns <u>match</u>, then they're the <u>same compound</u>. In this case the scientist can rule out <u>propanol</u> (because its spectrum is really <u>different</u> from the unknown spectrum). The spectra of methanol and ethanol look quite <u>similar</u> to the spectrum of the unknown compound. But on closer inspection you can see that the spectrum of the unknown sample and that of <u>methanol</u> are exactly the same — the unknown compound is methanol. Easy peasy.

Testing for Alcohol — Use Acidified Potassium Dichromate

<u>Acidified potassium dichromate</u> is used to test for the presence of <u>alcohol</u> in a sample:

1) Place the <u>sample</u> you want to test in a <u>test tube</u>.
2) Add a <u>few drops</u> of acidified potassium dichromate (this is <u>orange</u> in colour).
3) Then add a few drops of <u>silver nitrate</u>.
4) If the solution changes from <u>orange to green</u> then the sample <u>contains alcohol</u>.

Sometimes the police stop drivers who they suspect to be <u>drink driving</u>. They perform a test at the <u>roadside</u> to see if the driver is <u>over the limit</u>, and if so by how much — they do this using a <u>Breathalyser</u>. The device they use contains a small tube with <u>acidified potassium dichromate</u> and <u>silver nitrate</u>. If there's enough alcohol in the driver's <u>breath</u> then a positive result will be produced.

Don't drink and drive — you might damage your nine iron...

If you've never come across <u>infrared</u> before, don't worry — it gets explained in a lot <u>more detail</u> later on. All you need to know for <u>spectroscopy</u> is that all compounds absorb a <u>unique amount</u> and the amount that they absorb can be used to <u>identify the compound</u>. You'll also need to be able to <u>interpret spectra</u>.

Analytical Chemistry

Finally, the last page of qualitative chemistry — only another two more tests to go, phew.

Chromatography Can be Used to Separate Dyes

Chromatography can be used to determine the composition of a mixture, e.g. inks usually contain a mixture of different dyes. The different dyes in ink wash through paper at different rates. Chromatography uses this property to separate out the dyes.

Here's how it works...

1) Put spots of inks onto a pencil baseline on a sheet of filter paper.

2) Roll the sheet up and put it in a beaker with a bit of solvent (e.g. water) in the bottom.

3) The solvent seeps up the paper, carrying the ink dyes with it.

4) Each different dye will move up the paper at a different rate and form a spot in a different place.

5) You can compare an unknown ink to known inks to see which it is.

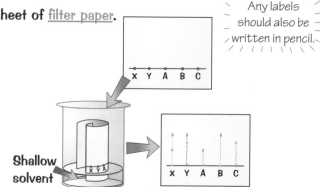

Any labels should also be written in pencil.

Shallow solvent

After doing a spot of shopping, Zoe thinks she was given a fake £10 note in her change — she decides to take it down to her local police station. The police investigate it and come up with four suspects. The forensic department is able to eliminate three suspects from their investigations using the results from this test.

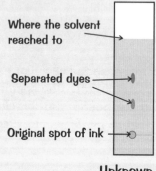

Where the solvent reached to

Separated dyes

Original spot of ink

Unknown ink   Ink A   Ink B   Ink C   Ink D

You can see from the position of the spots on the filter paper that the unknown ink has the same composition as ink B.

Testing for Simple Sugars — Use Benedict's Solution

To test for simple sugars:

1) Add blue Benedict's solution to the sample in a boiling tube. Then bring to the boil.

2) If there's an orange precipitate, that means the sample contains simple sugars, e.g. glucose, fructose, sucrose etc.

Sugar is often found in the urine of people with diabetes. If someone is suspected of having diabetes, their urine can be tested for sugars using Benedict's solution.

My mum found my chromatography mags under my bed...

So that's qualitative analysis — now you'll be able to identify pretty much any unknown sample and plus it's all good clean fun. At least you don't have to memorise what to add to what, and what all the different colours mean. On the next couple of pages the fun continues with quantitative analysis.

Analytical Chemistry

OK, onto quantitative analysis — concentration is important, for passing exams and for <u>chemistry solutions</u>.

Concentration <u>is Measured in</u> <u>g/dm³</u> <u>or in</u> <u>mol/dm³</u>

At some point you'll be asked to <u>prepare a solution</u> of a certain <u>concentration</u>.

1) There are <u>two</u> different <u>units</u> of concentration:

   - <u>grams per dm³</u> — **g/dm³** ← A '<u>dm³</u>' is a <u>decimetre cubed</u>. It's the same as a <u>litre</u> (1000 cm³).

   - <u>moles per dm³</u> — **mol/dm³** ← A <u>mole</u> is just a <u>number</u>. Mol/dm³ is to do with <u>how many molecules</u> of solute there are per litre of solution.

2) With concentration in g/dm³, you're saying what <u>mass</u> of solute is dissolved in <u>every dm³</u> of solvent.

3) E.g. to make 2 litres of 30 g/dm³ solution, you need to dissolve 60 g of solute (2 × 30 g) in water to make up 2 litres of solution. Not too bad. Here's another example, but for a smaller volume of solution:

Example <u>in g/dm³</u>

Dr Brine wants to prepare 500 cm³ of sodium chloride solution at 34 g/dm³ concentration. He has some dry sodium chloride and some water. Describe what he should do.

<u>ANSWER</u>:

He wants to make <u>half</u> a <u>dm³</u> of solution (500 cm³ is half a litre), so he needs 34 ÷ 2 = <u>17 g</u> of solute.

So he should weigh out <u>17 g</u> of sodium chloride and put it in a measuring cylinder, then add <u>water</u> until it he's got <u>500 cm³</u> and <u>stir</u> until it's all dissolved.

You Might Have to <u>Dilute</u> a Solution

You might be given a solution of, say, 3 mol/dm³ concentration and asked to prepare the same solution but in a different concentration, e.g. 0.25 mol/dm³. You'd have to 'water it down'. It's like making orange squash — but with sums and very careful measuring:

Example in mol/dm³

Beth has a <u>2.0 mol/dm³</u> solution of <u>hydrochloric acid</u> and some <u>water</u>. Describe how she could prepare <u>500 cm³</u> of a <u>0.5 mol/dm³</u> solution of hydrochloric acid.

1) Work out how many times the final concentration number goes into the original concentration number. (This tells you how much weaker the solution needs to be.)

2) Divide the FINAL VOLUME by this number — to work out the VOLUME OF ACID you need to use.

3) Subtract the VOLUME OF ACID from the FINAL VOLUME — to get the VOLUME OF WATER needed.

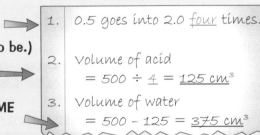

1. 0.5 goes into 2.0 <u>four</u> times.

2. Volume of acid = 500 ÷ <u>4</u> = <u>125 cm³</u>

3. Volume of water = 500 − 125 = <u>375 cm³</u>

<u>ANSWER</u>:

Beth should measure out 125 cm³ of 2.0 mol/dm³ acid in a measuring cylinder and 375 cm³ of water in another measuring cylinder, then add the acid to the water (in a beaker, conical flask or similar).

0.5 moles per decimetre cubed — how many holes can they dig?

With orange squash, you can just keep adding water till it <u>tastes</u> about right. You can't do that in GCSE Applied Science — because the solution you're making might well be poisonous, and because the concentration has to be <u>spot on</u>, not just 'about right'. So <u>measure</u> everything <u>very carefully</u>.

Analytical Chemistry

Imagine that some <u>sulfuric acid</u> has leaked into a river but no one knows <u>how much</u> of it. To find out, you could collect a sample of the river water and find out <u>how concentrated</u> the acid is — by doing a <u>titration</u>.

Titrations are Used to Find Out Concentrations

Doing a titration means finding out <u>what volume of acid</u> is needed to <u>neutralise</u> a known <u>volume</u> and <u>concentration</u> of alkali. (It can be the other way round — finding the volume of alkali needed, if you know about the acid.) Then a quick <u>sum</u> (see next page) is all you need to find the mystery <u>concentration</u>.

Setting Up the Apparatus

1) Use a <u>pipette</u> and <u>pipette filler</u> to measure out the right volume of <u>alkali</u> (often 25 cm³) into a <u>conical flask</u>. Make sure you note down the <u>concentration</u> of the alkali.

2) Add two or three drops of <u>indicator</u> to the alkali.

3) Use a <u>funnel</u> to fill a <u>burette</u> with the acid. Make sure it's filled <u>exactly</u> to the level marked at the top. (Do this with the top of the burette <u>below eye level</u> — you don't want to be looking up if some acid spills over.)

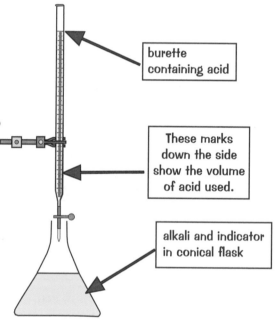

burette containing acid

These marks down the side show the volume of acid used.

alkali and indicator in conical flask

Doing the Titration

1) Using the <u>burette</u>, add the <u>acid</u> to the alkali a bit at a time, giving the conical flask a regular <u>swirl</u>.

2) When you think the <u>end-point</u> (colour change) is about to be reached, go especially slowly — drip by drip.

3) When the indicator <u>changes colour</u>, all the alkali has been <u>neutralised</u> and you should <u>stop adding acid</u>.

4) <u>Read</u> the burette to see what volume of acid you've added to the alkali. Take the reading at eye level, and remember — it's the level of the <u>bottom of the meniscus</u> that matters.

Remember, you can also do titrations the other way round — adding alkali to acid.

Repeat the Experiment

With titrations, as with many of life's most enjoyable experiences, <u>once just isn't enough</u>.

You need to get several consistent readings

To increase the <u>accuracy</u> of your titration and to spot any <u>anomalous results</u>, you need <u>several consistent readings</u>.

- The <u>first</u> titration you do should be a <u>rough titration</u> to get an <u>approximate idea</u> of where the solution changes colour (the end-point).

- You then need to <u>repeat</u> the whole thing a few times, making sure you get (pretty much) the <u>same answer</u> each time (within about 0.2 cm³).

Titrations — not funny, but useful...

Before the end of this unit, you'll be a dab hand at titrations — whether you want to be or not. They're not too tricky really — you just need to make sure that your results are as <u>accurate</u> as possible, which means <u>going slowly near the end-point</u> and then <u>repeating the whole process</u>.

Analytical Chemistry

So you've done the titration — now for the sums.

You Might be Asked to Calculate the Concentration

The whole point of doing a titration is so you can use the results to work out the concentration of an acid or alkali.

Example 1

Brian did the following experiment to work out the concentration of a sample of hydrochloric acid.

He put 20 cm³ of sodium hydroxide solution, concentration 0.1 mol/dm³, in a conical flask. He did a titration and found that 40 cm³ of hydrochloric acid was needed to neutralise the sodium hydroxide.

Work out the concentration of Brian's hydrochloric acid.

> The balanced equation for the reaction in Brian's experiment is: $NaOH + HCl \longrightarrow NaCl + H_2O$
>
> 1) This means there's one 'HCl' used to neutralise one 'NaOH'.
>
> 2) But in Brian's experiment, 40 cm³ of HCl neutralised 20 cm³ of NaOH.
>   He needed more acid than alkali — so the acid must have been more dilute.
>
> 3 In fact, he needed twice as much acid...
>
> 4) ...so its concentration must have been half that of the alkali.
>   So the hydrochloric acid had a concentration of 0.1 mol/dm³ ÷ 2 = 0.05 mol/dm³.

Example 2

Professor Plum had a different sample of hydrochloric acid. He found that 30 cm³ of acid was needed to neutralise 25 cm³ of 1 mol/dm³ sodium hydroxide solution. Calculate the concentration of the acid.

The volumes aren't as easy to compare this time. But, you can do it using numbers of moles instead:

Step 1: Work out how many moles of the "known" substance (i.e. the sodium hydroxide) you have, using this formula triangle:

Concentration (in mol/dm³) Number of moles

$$\dfrac{n}{c \times V}$$

Volume (in dm³)
One dm³ is a litre

Number of moles = concentration × volume
= 1 mol/dm³ × (25 / 1000) dm³
= 0.025 moles of NaOH

Remember: 1000 cm³ = 1 dm³

Step 2: Work out how many moles of the "unknown" stuff you must have had using the equation.

The equation's the same as above — one HCl for one NaOH, so you must have equal numbers of moles (of HCl and NaOH). So you must have 0.025 moles of HCl.

Step 3: Find the concentration of the "unknown" substance (i.e. the acid) using the same formula triangle as used above.

Concentration = number of moles ÷ volume
= 0.025 ÷ (30 / 1000) dm³
= 0.833 mol/dm³.

Check that your answers are sensible. In this case, you needed a bit more acid than alkali, so you'd expect the acid to be a bit less concentrated.

Concentrate on your calculations...

You need to be pretty careful with these calculations — always check that your answer is realistic.
If you're given the volume of anything in cm³ you need to convert it to dm³ (because that's what the equation uses). It's pretty easy really — just divide the number by 1000 (see p.28 for more).

Investigating Properties of Materials

Materials scientists investigate the way substances behave in various conditions. They investigate the properties of materials, and use their results to suggest which materials are best for different jobs.

Materials Conduct Electricity Well If They Have Low Resistance

Say you're designing a robot to explore the surface of Mars. It'll need lots of electrical circuits to control its movement, cameras, data recording, etc. The various components (bits) of the circuits will need to be made of different materials depending on what they do.

1) Some materials conduct (carry) electricity better than others. E.g. copper conducts electricity well (that's why it's used for wiring in household circuits).

2) A 'good conductor' is a material that doesn't offer much resistance to the flow of electrical current.

3) Different substances have different electrical resistances. A materials scientist could find out the resistance of a new material or component using a test circuit.

You Can Use a Test Circuit to Work Out Resistance

With this circuit, you can measure the voltage across a component and the current flowing through it.

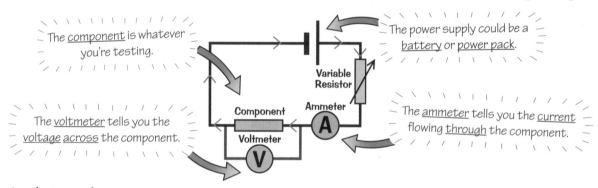

The component is whatever you're testing.

The power supply could be a battery or power pack.

Variable Resistor

The voltmeter tells you the voltage across the component.

Component

Ammeter

The ammeter tells you the current flowing through the component.

Voltmeter

Here's what you do:

1) Use the variable resistor to adjust the current to, say, 0.5 A.

2) Read the voltage from the voltmeter.

3) Record your current and voltage readings in a nice table.

4) Use the variable resistor again to change the current to, say, 1.0 A. Record the new voltage across the component.

5) Keep on doing this until you've got several readings. (See the next page for why you should do this.)

Current (A)	Voltage (V)
0.5	2.4
1.0	

Once you know the current and voltage, working out resistance is fairly easy. Use this equation:

$$\text{Resistance} = \frac{\text{Voltage}}{\text{Current}}$$

EXAMPLE:

Current = 0.5 A, Voltage = 2.4 V.
So resistance = 2.4 ÷ 0.5 = 4.8 Ω.

This is the symbol for ohms — the ohm is the unit of resistance.

Test me — I won't resist...

The wire used in most electrical circuits has a very low resistance. If a fault develops in a circuit so that the only components are the power supply and some wire, it's called a short circuit. Short circuits can be dangerous — you can get a huge current (because of the low resistance), overheating, and a fire.

Investigating Properties of Materials

Sometimes it's useful if the resistance of a component changes as the conditions change. E.g. electrical thermometers work because the resistance of one of their components changes as the temperature varies.

Some Devices Have Constant Resistance...

Say you've tested a component (see the previous page), done the sums to work out resistance, and these are your results.

Current, I (in A)	1	2	3	4
Voltage, V (in V)	2.5	5.0	7.5	10.0
Resistance, R (in Ω)	2.5	2.5	2.5	2.5

1) The resistance, R, is constant as the current increases.

2) If you plot current against voltage, you get a straight line through the origin — so you can see that the current is proportional to the voltage.

...And Some Have Variable Resistance

Not all components have a fixed resistance. For a filament lamp, the results would be a bit like this:

Current, I (in A)	1	2	3	4
Voltage, V (in V)	2.0	5.0	10.0	36.0
Resistance, R (in Ω)	2.0	2.5	3.3	9.0

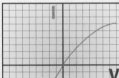

1) The resistance isn't constant — it increases as the current increases.
2) This is because the bigger the current through the filament lamp, the hotter it gets. And as its temperature increases, its resistance increases.
3) The graph's a curve — the current is not proportional to the voltage.

Resistance Depends on Length, Thickness and Material

A component in a circuit can be designed to have a certain resistance. Take a piece of wire, for example:

- When you build circuits in the lab, the wire you use is probably fairly thin, made of copper, and often comes in ready-made lengths (coated with black or red plastic insulation, with crocodile clips at either end).

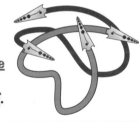

- If these wires were thicker, longer or made of different material, their resistance would be different. You might have to investigate how the resistance of a component is affected by its length and thickness, as well as what it's made of.

EXAMPLE: Investigating how thickness affects resistance.

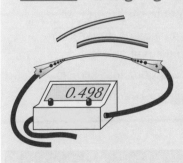

1) Use the standard test circuit, with a piece of wire as the 'component'.
2) Take several current and voltage readings (as on the previous page), then calculate the resistance for each one and work out the average (this gives you a much more reliable result than just doing it once).
3) Repeat step 2 with several pieces of wire of different thicknesses. All these pieces of wire must be the same length and made of the same material — so you can be sure it's the change in thickness which is causing any change in resistance.

- Different materials have different resistances — there's no hard and fast rule. For any one material, though, you should find that thicker wires have lower resistance but longer wires have higher resistance.

I'm not thick — I just have a low resistance...

With experiments like the one above, never just take one reading — take several (at least three). Then you'll spot whether the resistance is constant or variable — which is important. And if it's constant, you can use all those readings to take an average — just add them all up and divide by how many there are.

Investigating Properties of Materials

Materials scientists consider <u>physical properties</u> like density and strength as well as electrical properties like resistance. For instance, when you're building a <u>house</u>, choosing materials with the right physical properties is very important. E.g. we don't build houses from <u>chocolate</u> because it <u>melts</u> in warm weather.

Thermal Conductivity <u>Means</u> How Well <u>Materials</u> Conduct Heat

1) <u>Thermal conductivity</u> means how well a substance <u>conducts heat</u>. If the <u>walls of your house</u> had a <u>high</u> thermal conductivity, you'd be 'losing' a lot of heat to the air outside — which would be wasteful and expensive. It's better to build the walls of a house from materials with <u>low</u> thermal conductivity.

2) Here's a simple way to compare the <u>thermal conductivity</u> of <u>different materials</u>:

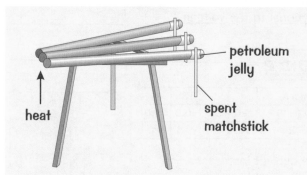

- Put three rods, all the <u>same size</u> but made of <u>different materials</u>, on a tripod, with a spent (used) matchstick stuck to one end with petroleum jelly.
- <u>Heat</u> the rods at the other end and time how long it takes each matchstick to fall off.
- The <u>sooner</u> a matchstick <u>falls off</u>, the quicker the heat has been conducted along the rod — so the <u>higher</u> the <u>thermal conductivity</u> of that material.

<u>You'll Need to</u> Compare the Densities <u>of</u> Different Materials

1) <u>Density</u> means how much <u>mass</u> there is in a certain <u>volume</u> of material. The more mass per cm^3, say, the higher the density of the material — the more stuff is packed into the same space.

2) For example, imagine you're making a nice <u>cup of tea</u>. Now imagine you have two <u>teaspoons</u> exactly the same size and shape, but one's made of <u>steel</u> and the other one's made of <u>plastic</u>. The <u>steel</u> teaspoon would be a lot heavier — because steel is <u>denser</u> than plastic.

3) To work out the <u>density</u> of an object (like a teaspoon) you have to know its <u>mass</u> and its <u>volume</u>.

4) <u>Mass</u> is fairly easy to find — just use a <u>balance</u> to find the mass in grams (g).

5) Finding the <u>volume</u> of a funny-shaped object (like a teaspoon) is a bit harder. Here's how:

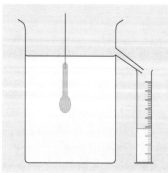

- Fill a <u>displacement can</u> with water (overfill it first and let water spill out — it will stop at the level shown opposite).
- Lower your test sample into the can (on a piece of thread). As you do this, water will spill into the measuring cylinder.
- This 'overspill' water has been 'displaced' by your test sample.
- The volume of <u>water</u> in the <u>measuring cylinder</u> is equal to the <u>volume of the test sample</u>. Clever.

6) Use this formula to calculate the density of the sample.

   <u>EXAMPLE</u>: Mass = 14.92 g, Volume = 1.9 cm^3.
   So <u>density</u> = 14.92 ÷ 1.9 = <u>7.85 g/cm^3</u>.

$$\text{Density}_{\text{(in g/cm}^3)} = \frac{\text{Mass (in g)}}{\text{Volume (in cm}^3)}$$

Thermal conductivity — for pyjama-wearing orchestras...

You could find out your own density using the same method — weigh yourself to find your <u>mass</u>, then fill a bath to the top and get in (completely underwater) to find your <u>volume</u> — measure how much water spills over the top. You'll need to have a pretty big measuring cylinder though, to avoid floods.

Investigating Properties of Materials

Just as some people are stronger than others, some materials are stronger than others. And before building a tower block, say, it's a good idea to find some nice strong materials to build it with.

Testing Strength — Finding the 'Breaking Point'

1) There are different kinds of strength, e.g. how hard it is to crush something by pressing down on it, how hard it is to snap something by stretching it. Depending on what a material's being used for, one kind of strength will probably be more important.

2) E.g. the wires used to winch people onto rescue helicopters need to be strong in the sense of not snapping when heavy objects are dangled from them.

3) You could test materials for this kind of strength using the equipment shown below.

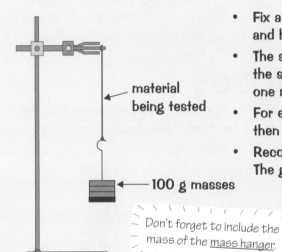

material being tested

100 g masses

Don't forget to include the mass of the mass hanger.

- Fix a sample of each material to a clamp stand, as shown, and hang a mass hanger from the other end.

- The samples of each different material must all be exactly the same size and shape. E.g. if you're testing wires, each one must be the same length and the same thickness.

- For each sample, start off with the mass hanger empty, then add 100 g masses one by one until the sample breaks.

- Record the mass needed to break each sample. The greater that mass, the stronger the material.

Material	A	B	C
Breaking mass (g)	700	700	900

You Could Make Your Results More Precise

From the results above, it looks like wire A and wire B have exactly the same strength — but this isn't necessarily the case:

1) You know that 700 g was enough to break wire A, but it might have broken with a load of only 690 g, or 640 g, or 610 g — you can't tell from these results. It's the same thing for wire B.

2) So it could be that both materials are equally strong — but it could be that material A is stronger than B, or it could be that material A is weaker than material B. You'd have to do another experiment...

3) Repeat the experiment, but for wires A and B put 600 g on the hanger straight away, then add smaller masses — just 10 g at a time, say, rather than 100 g.

4) To get a more precise result for wire C, you could put 800 g on straight away, then add 10 g at a time.

5) The results from this second experiment might look something like this. These results are much more precise and you can now tell that material A is stronger than material B.

A	B	C
680 g	620 g	850 g

Working out strength — go to the gym...

When you're doing experiments, remember — only change one thing at a time. E.g. in the experiment above, each sample must be the same length and thickness. If you tested a thin copper wire and a thicker bronze wire, you wouldn't know what made the difference in strength — the type of material or the thickness.

Recording and Presenting Data

Well, by now you should have your standard procedure sorted and be more than familiar with the equipment that you'll be using. But it'll all be a waste of time if you don't record your results properly.

Always Use Tables to Record Results

The easiest way to record data during an experiment is by using a table.

1) Think about the data you're going to record and draw the table before you start — you should include columns for the data you are going to calculate (e.g. resistance) as well as the data you are going to measure (e.g. current and voltage).

2) Make sure you label your table clearly, showing what you are measuring and the units.

Length of wire (cm)	Voltage (volts, V)	Current (amps, I)	Resistance (ohms, Ω)
20			
40			
60			

It's important to keep your results table neat and tidy so that you can make sense of it when the experiment is finished. It'd all be a waste of time if you couldn't read your results.

Use Bar Charts to Present Discrete Data

1) Bar charts are used to present discrete data. This can be either discrete numbers or different categories, e.g. type of antibiotic (so you wouldn't use a bar chart to represent percentages).

Discrete data is data that can be measured exactly, e.g. number of people — you can't really have half a person or 2.2 people. Continuous data is data that can only be measured to a given degree of accuracy, e.g. a person's weight — this could be 76 kg, 52 kg, 64.2 kg. You'll never get an exact value because there'll always be a more accurate way of measuring, e.g. to the nearest g, mg or μg.

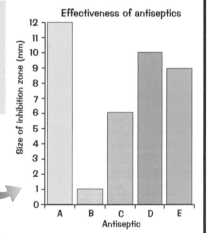

2) The width of the bars on a bar chart is always the same, but the heights of the bars vary to represent the data.

3) There should be a gap between each bar.

This chart shows the size of inhibition zones with different antiseptics.

Use Histograms to Present Continuous Data

1) Histograms are used to present continuous data in different categories. They're tricky, but there's more about them in our GCSE Maths books (shameless plug).

2) The width of the bars can stay the same or vary to represent the size of the category.

3) The areas of the bars vary to represent the size of data.

Diameter of bacterial colony (mm)	Number of colonies	Frequency density of colonies
0-2	14	7
2-5	9	3
5-10	6	1.2
10-15	5	1
15-20	2	0.4

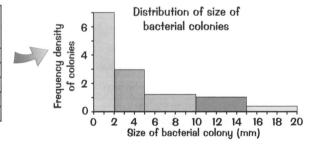

Pictograms can be used to present data in a visually appealing way.

1) They're bar charts or histograms where the bars have been replaced by pictures to represent the data.

2) The size or the number of pictures varies with the data.

3) You need to include a key to explain what the pictures mean.

Recording and Presenting Data

Use Pie Charts to Present Data as Proportions of a Whole

1) Pie charts are used to present data as proportions (percentages or fractions) of a whole. You'd never use them to represent raw data.

2) The 'pie' is divided into segments that represent proportions of the whole.

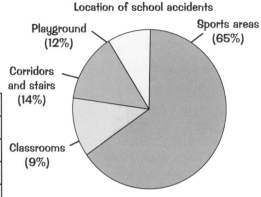

Location of school accidents

Playground (12%)   Sports areas (65%)

Corridors and stairs (14%)

Classrooms (9%)

You can draw pie charts using a pie chart measurer or a protractor (though you'll need to convert each value into an angle).

Area of school	% of accidents
Sports areas	65
Playground	12
Corridors and stairs	14
Classrooms	9

Use Graphs to Show the Relationship Between Variables

1) You should use graphs when investigating the effect of one variable on another. They shouldn't be used when the data is in different categories. Note the difference between the following example (where the same antiseptic is being used but in different concentrations) and the bar chart on the previous page (where five different antiseptics were being used).

2) The variable that you change (e.g. the concentration of antiseptic used, or the length of wire used) is called the independent variable. This should be plotted on the x-axis (the horizontal axis).

3) The variable which is being measured (e.g. the size of the inhibition zone or the resistance of a piece of wire) is called the dependent variable and is plotted on the y-axis (the vertical axis).

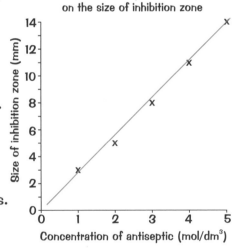

The effect of antiseptic concentration on the size of inhibition zone

4) Points on a graph can be joined up to make straight or curved lines. Don't forget that any line you draw is only really an educated guess — the data could do anything between the two points you measured.

5) The shape of the line shows the relationship between the variables.

6) Often a 'line of best fit' is drawn — which goes through (or close to) most of the points on the graph.

7) Make sure your graphs have titles, their axes are labelled, and the scales are appropriate.

Other Visual Images can also be Useful

If it's appropriate, data can be represented in other ways — here are some examples:

1) Radar charts are a 'clock-face' form of bar chart — the bars radiate from a central point.

2) Bubble charts use circles of different sizes to display data.

3) Cartograms have graphs or charts placed on a map — they show how data relates to an area.

4) Combination charts — two charts in one, e.g. a bar chart and a line graph placed on the same axes.

5) Diagrams and sketches can be useful — remember to label drawings and include a scale.

6) Photographs or video footage can also be used to display results in a very visually appealing way.

Pie chart — a new entry at number two: meat and potato...

Sorry to go on, but I just can't stress this enough — don't forget to label your axes and add a title.

Calculations and Analysis

Sometimes you need to <u>convert</u> your results into different <u>units</u> so you can use them in <u>formulas</u>.

For Some Calculations You Need to Change the Units

Here's an example of how you change the units for <u>mass</u> (formulas with mass in normally need the units to be <u>kilograms</u> (kg)).

| microgram (μg) |
| milligram (mg) |
| gram (g) |
| kilogram (kg) |

There are <u>1000 μg</u> in a <u>milligram</u>, so to convert 1 microgram into mg you ÷1000.

There are <u>1000 mg</u> in a <u>gram</u>, so to convert 1 milligram into grams you ÷1000.

There are <u>1000 g</u> in a <u>kilogram</u>, so to convert 1 gram into kilograms you ÷1000.

Similar rules apply if you're going the <u>other way</u>. You just <u>multiply</u> instead of <u>divide</u>. E.g. if you have 5.2 kg of salt and want to know how many grams that is, you'd multiply by 1000: 5.2 × 1000 = 5200 g.

> The words <u>before</u> the unit tell you how big it is.
> E.g. <u>kilo</u> means that there's <u>1000</u> of the unit
> (<u>kilo</u>gram = 1000 grams). <u>Milli</u> means <u>one</u>
> <u>thousandth</u> (<u>milli</u>gram = one thousandth of a gram).

> So, if you want to convert a SMALL
> unit to a BIGGER one you DIVIDE.
> If you want to convert a BIG unit to
> a SMALLER one you MULTIPLY.

You Need to Know These Units

1) <u>Volume</u> — Most formulas use <u>cubic decimetres</u>. There are 1000 <u>cubic decimetres</u> (dm³) in one <u>cubic metre</u> (m³), 1000 <u>cubic centimetres</u> (cm³) in a cubic decimetre and 1000 <u>cubic millimetres</u> (mm³) in a cubic centimetre.

2) <u>Length</u> — Most formulas use <u>metres</u>. There are 1000 <u>metres</u> (m) in one <u>kilometre</u> (km), 100 <u>centimetres</u> (cm) in a metre, 10 <u>millimetres</u> (mm) in a centimetre and 1000 <u>micrometres</u> (μm) in a millimetre.

3) <u>Time</u> — Most formulas use <u>seconds</u> (there are <u>60</u> seconds in a minute). To convert <u>minutes</u> (min) to seconds (s) you need to <u>multiply by 60</u>. To convert <u>hours</u> (h) into minutes you also <u>multiply by 60</u>.

4) <u>Temperature</u> is measured in <u>degrees Celsius</u> (°C). (You won't need to convert it into any other form.)

> 1 dm³ is the same as
> 1 litre. 1 cm³ is the
> same as a millilitre (ml).

Here are some physics units you need to know:

1) <u>Current</u> — measured in <u>amperes</u> (A), there are 1000 <u>milliamperes</u> (mA) in one ampere.

2) <u>Resistance</u> — measured in <u>ohms</u> (Ω), there are 1000 ohms in a <u>kilohm</u> (kΩ) and 1000 kΩ in a <u>megohm</u> (MΩ).

3) <u>Energy</u> — measured in <u>joules</u> (J), there are 1000 J in one <u>kilojoule</u> (kJ).

4) <u>Energy supplied</u> — measured in <u>kilowatt-hour</u> (kW-h).

5) <u>Power</u> — measured in <u>watts</u> (W), there are 1000 W in one <u>kilowatt</u> (kW).

6) <u>Density</u> — measured in <u>grams per cubic centimetre</u> (g/cm³) or <u>kilograms per cubic metre</u> (kg/m³).

7) <u>Voltage</u> (or potential difference) — measured in <u>volts</u> (V).

8) <u>Force</u> — measured in <u>newtons</u> (N).

There aren't as many units used in chemistry, but you still need to learn a few:

1) <u>Chemical quantity</u> — measured in <u>moles</u> (mol).

2) <u>Concentration</u> — measured in <u>grams per cubic decimetre</u> (g/dm³), which is the same as <u>grams per litre</u> (g/l). Concentration can also be measured in <u>moles per cubic decimetre</u> (mol/dm³).

My friend's really rich — he lives in a megohm...

Remember, if there's a <u>kilo before the unit</u>, then there's <u>1000</u> of that unit. Easy peasy.

Calculations and Analysis

It's all very well collecting all your data and making it look nice with pretty little graphs, but you also need to be able to interpret your results and spot if any of them look a bit odd.

Repeat Experiments and Take an Average of the Results

You should repeat experiments at least three times, and take an average of the results
— this improves reliability and helps you spot any 'anomalous' results (i.e. results that don't seem right).

1) Look for any anomalous results.

2) Repeat experiments that produced anomalous results.

3) Add up the consistent readings.

4) Divide the total by the number of readings to give the average.

Investigating the effect of wire length on resistance

Repeat	Length of wire (cm)	Voltage (V)	Current (A)
1	10.0	0.60	0.95
2	10.0	0.60	0.94
3	10.0	0.60	0.76
4	10.0	0.60	0.92
		Average	0.94

EXAMPLE — working out the average resistance:

1) The third repeat gave a much lower result than the others — this result is anomalous.

2) The experiment has been repeated (repeat 4).

3) Add up repeats 1, 2 and 4: (0.95 + 0.94 + 0.92 = 2.81).

4) Calculate the average: 2.81 ÷ 3 = 0.94 A

Analyse Your Results Using Calculations, Graphs and Charts

Once you have finished the experiment and calculated the average of your results, you may need to use calculations to analyse your results. This means using formulas to convert data into more useful forms.

Length of wire (cm)	Voltage (V)	Average current (A)	Resistance (Ω)
10.0	0.60	0.94	0.64
20.0	0.60	0.43	1.40
30.0	0.60	0.29	2.07
40.0	0.60	0.20	3.00

EXAMPLE — work out resistance from readings of current and voltage using the formula $V = I \times R$.
You need to rearrange the formula to get resistance $(R = V \div I)$. For the 10 cm wire:
$R = 0.6 \div 0.94 = 0.64 \, \Omega$

Once your results are in a useful format you might want to plot them on a graph or chart. You'll need to think about:

1) The type of graph or chart you choose to display your results.

2) A suitable scale. Make sure you plot all points correctly.

3) Whether or not a line of best fit is appropriate.

4) Any anomalies (results that don't look right), and trends or patterns in the results.

EXAMPLE

1) A graph has been drawn because we're investigating the relationship between two variables (i.e. the effect of wire length on resistance).

2) The maximum resistance is 3 Ω, so increments of 0.5 Ω gave a suitable scale (anything bigger would've made the graph too small).

3) A line of best fit was drawn to show the trend.

4) As the length of the wire was increased the resistance also increased.

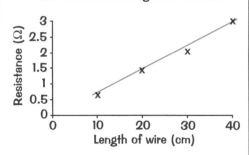

The effect of wire length on resistance

None of my results are anomalous — they all have names...

Getting your chart or graph right is crucial. But, first you need to decide which type to draw. Remember, if you're investigating the relationship between variables then you should draw a graph (see p.27 for more).

Conclusions and Evaluations

Planning an experiment isn't too bad and carrying it out can be quite fun — but the worst part, without a shadow of a doubt, is evaluating — picking holes in your own work just isn't natural, but it has to be done.

Conclusions **Should** Summarise **and** Explain **Results**

At the end of your investigation you need to include a conclusion. You should:

1) State what your results show.
2) Describe your graphs or charts.
3) Identify any patterns or trends.
4) Explain your conclusions using science — the more understanding you show the better.

> EXAMPLE
>
> 1) The results show that the longer the piece of wire the greater the resistance.
>
> 2) The graph has a straight line, which means that the resistance and the length of the wire have a linear relationship.
>
> 3) The graph shows that resistance increases by approximately 0.75 Ω for every 10 cm of wire.
>
> 4) Resistance is a measure of how hard it is for current to flow around a circuit. The longer the wire, the harder it is for current to flow. So the longer the wire, the higher the resistance.

Evaluations — **Describe** How **You Could** Improve **It**

1) Comment on your method — was the equipment suitable?
   Did the procedure allow you to obtain accurate results?

2) Comment on the quality of your results — did you get enough evidence to reach a conclusion? Were your results reliable?

3) Identify any anomalies in your results — if there were none then say so.

4) Try to explain any anomalies — were they caused by errors in measurement?
   Were there any other variables that could have affected your results?

5) Suggest any changes that would improve your investigation — is there more suitable equipment you could have used? What further work could provide additional evidence to support your conclusions?

I'd value this E somewhere in the region of 250-300k

> EXAMPLE
>
> 1) The equipment and method used were suitable and produced accurate results. But the degree of accuracy might have been affected by the voltmeter and ammeter (if they weren't calibrated properly). There may also have been a slight variation in the thickness of the wire.
>
> 2) The results were reliable. Each experiment was repeated and calculations were carried out on the average readings for each length. The number of readings taken was enough to reach a valid conclusion.
>
> 3) One of the results for 10 cm of wire was anomalous. This experiment had to be repeated.
>
> 4) The anomalous result could have been caused by an error in the measurement of the length of the wire, a difference in the thickness of the wire, or an error when taking readings from the ammeter or voltmeter.
>
> 5) If the experiment was carried out again then no changes would be made to the equipment or procedure used, but extra care would be taken when measuring the lengths of wires.
>   Other experiments could be carried out, e.g. testing more lengths or keeping the length of wire the same but changing the thickness.

I like experimentation — draw your own conclusions...

And that's pretty much that. By now you should know everything there is to know about carrying out a scientific investigation. I hope you've been paying attention because you're going to have to do it yourself. If you're still a bit uncertain there's more help on writing up an investigation on page 134.

Report: Developing Scientific Skills 2

It's all very well being a genius with a burette, but you'll get no marks unless you <u>write up</u> your experiments.

You Need to Write Six Reports About Practical Activities

You need to write SIX reports about practical activities — one for each of these areas:
1) Microscopy,
2) Microorganisms,
3) Qualitative chemical analysis,
4) Quantitative chemical analysis,
5) Electrical properties,
6) Other physical properties.

These reports will make up the rest of your portfolio for <u>UNIT 1: DEVELOPING SCIENTIFIC SKILLS</u>.

<u>Each report</u> will be a <u>WRITE-UP</u> of the activity. For each activity, include:
- a <u>risk assessment</u> and a <u>description of what you did</u>,
- your <u>results</u>,
- <u>analysis</u> of your results and a <u>conclusion</u>,
- an <u>evaluation</u> of the activity.

It's important to evaluate your activity.

Include a Risk Assessment and Describe What You Did

1) Before you start each activity, <u>read the instructions</u> for it and do a <u>risk assessment</u> (see p.2).
2) Choose the <u>right equipment</u> and <u>set it up carefully</u> (see p.8-p.11).
3) Write a <u>list</u> of all the equipment you're going to use, and draw <u>labelled diagrams</u> where appropriate.

Make Measurements and Present Your Results Carefully

1) Do the activity, following any instructions step by step. You're marked on the <u>accuracy</u> of your observations, so you need to take measurements <u>carefully</u> and record your results in tables, etc.
2) Remember to <u>repeat</u> observations and measurements where necessary:
   - repeating tests and working out an <u>average</u> will give you a <u>more reliable result</u>,
   - if a result seems obviously <u>wrong</u>, do the test again (and write down <u>why</u> you're repeating it).
3) <u>Present your results</u> sensibly — tables, charts, graphs, etc. (See p.26-p.27. for help with these.)

Identify Relationships in Your Conclusion

1) Your data might not be very <u>useful</u> in its 'raw' form — you might have to do some <u>calculations</u> (p.29).
2) Look for <u>patterns</u> in your results, e.g. straight lines on graphs, and say what they mean. <u>Explain</u> your findings using your <u>science knowledge</u>.
3) Draw an overall <u>conclusion</u> — say what the <u>evidence</u> from your experiment has shown (see p.30).

Evaluate the Activity

<u>Evaluate</u> what you've done, e.g. how <u>reliable</u> do you think your data is? Was there anything that might have caused an error? How could you make your investigation <u>better</u>?

Develop your scientific skills — try juggling with burettes...*

Practical activities are nothing to be scared of — often, it's just a case of <u>following instructions</u> and <u>taking measurements carefully</u> — then <u>recording everything clearly</u> (see p.26).   *Actually, no, don't.

Products from Living Things

All our food comes from living things (vegetables from plants, meat from animals, etc.) so we'd be pretty stuffed without them. Microorganisms also play a part in making food and drink...

Fermentation in Yeast Makes Alcohol

Fermentation is the process of converting sugar to alcohol or acid.
It's an anaerobic process — that means it happens when there's no oxygen present.

See p.57 for more on microorganisms.

1) Fermentation in yeast converts sugar into alcohol and carbon dioxide:

> glucose → ethanol (alcohol) + carbon dioxide

2) Yeast contains enzymes that speed up the reaction.

3) Enzymes are biological catalysts — they speed up reactions without being changed or used up.

4) Without them, some reactions (like fermentation) would be too slow to be useful.

Yeast is used to make some food and drink products...

Bread

Yeast is added to bread dough. The carbon dioxide produced causes the bread to rise — forming little holes that make it nice and light.

Alcoholic drinks

Fermentation of yeast is used to make wine and beer. The yeast converts sugar (from the grapes or barley) into alcohol.

Fermentation in Bacteria Makes Acid

Fermentation doesn't only occur in yeast. Bacteria do it too — but they produce acid not alcohol. Bacteria are used in both cheese and yoghurt production. Enzymes in bacteria convert the sugar present in milk into acid.

Cheese

Bacteria produce solid curds in the milk. More bacteria are added to the curds, and the whole lot is left to ripen for a while.

Yoghurt

The acid causes the milk to clot and solidify into yoghurt. Then flavours (e.g. fruit) and colours are sometimes added before the yoghurt is packaged.

Fermentation Needs the Right Conditions

For these processes to work well the conditions need to be just right.
The enzymes in the bacteria or yeast need:

1) The right temperature.

2) Enough sugar.

3) An environment with no oxygen.

If the conditions aren't right the yeast or bacteria won't work quickly enough or may even die.

Invite yeast to parties — they're fun guys...

So, when you go to a posh restaurant and have a nice slice of grilled panini you're actually eating slightly burnt fermented dough mixture full of carbon dioxide... mmm... though I suppose if it said that on the menu you wouldn't actually order it. Anyone for acidified, curdled milk on toast? No?

Products from Living Things

So, we've living things to thank for tasty foods, but it doesn't stop there, oh no.
You'll be amazed at just how much we depend on other living organisms...

We Get Other Useful Products from Living Organisms

There are three types of organism, and they all make useful products for human beings:

Plants

1) Cotton — can be used to make fabric (for clothes, curtains, etc.)
It's made from a fibre that comes from the cotton plant.

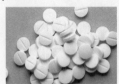

2) Pigments — used to make dyes to colour material, some of these also come from plants. E.g. indigo is a blue/purple pigment that can be used to colour clothes. It comes from various plants.

3) Drugs — some of the chemicals used to make drugs can be extracted from plants. E.g. aspirin can be made from a substance found in willow bark, and morphine can be made from a substance found in a type of poppy (see page 64).

Animals

1) Leather — animal hides (usually those of cows) are used for clothing and upholstery.

2) Wool — the 'fur' of sheep or goats can be spun into threads that can be woven together to make wool. It's mainly used for clothing.

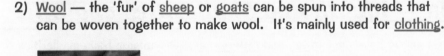

3) Silk — a fibre from the cocoons of silkworm larvae can be made into a luxurious fabric used for clothing.

Microorganisms

1) Food — remember that microorganisms are used in the production of bread, beer, wine, cheese and yoghurt (see the previous page). Fungi can be used to make some vegetarian meat substitutes.

2) Medicine — microorganisms can be used to make antibiotics, e.g. penicillin is produced by a fungus. The enzymes in most fungi need the same conditions as fermentation (see the previous page).

Microorganisms making medicine — now I've heard it all...

It might be hard to believe but those nasty little blighters that can make you ill (see p.57) can also make you better again. Penicillin was discovered by Alexander Fleming and it was really important in World War II. It was used to treat bacterial infection, which reduced the need for amputations and saved thousands of lives.

Cells and Classification

All living things are made from <u>cells</u> — they're the very basic '<u>building blocks</u>' of life. You, me and that dying plant in the corner of your bedroom are all made up from these cells. Each cell is made up of lots of <u>chemical compounds</u>.

Plant Cells and Animal Cells Have Their Differences

You need to identify animal and plant cells and all their different parts.

Animal Cell

Plant Cell

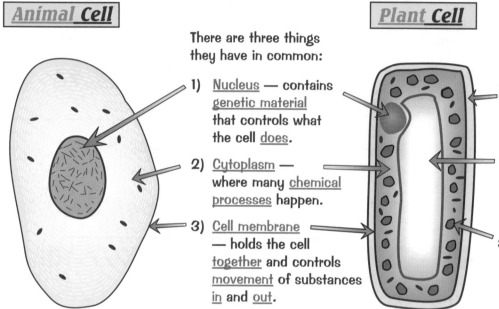

There are three things they have in common:

1) <u>Nucleus</u> — contains <u>genetic material</u> that controls what the cell <u>does</u>.

2) <u>Cytoplasm</u> — where many <u>chemical processes</u> happen.

3) <u>Cell membrane</u> — holds the cell <u>together</u> and controls <u>movement</u> of substances <u>in</u> and <u>out</u>.

And three extras that only plant cells have:

1) <u>Cell wall</u> — made of <u>cellulose</u>, provides <u>support</u> for the cell.

2) <u>Large, permanent vacuole</u> — contains <u>cell sap</u>, and helps provide <u>support</u>.

3) <u>Chloroplasts</u> — absorb light energy for <u>photosynthesis</u>. Found in the green parts of plants.

Classification — Identifying Similarities and Differences

The plant and animal cells above have <u>similarities</u> and <u>differences</u>. Organisms have <u>similarities</u> and <u>differences</u> in their <u>whole bodies</u> as well as in their cells — scientists use these similarities and differences to <u>classify</u> organisms.

1) Scientists classify organisms into groups based on <u>physical similarities</u>. For example, organisms that have chloroplasts and make their own food by photosynthesis are plants. The classification system is based on <u>similarities</u> like this.

2) Living things are divided into <u>kingdoms</u> (e.g. the animal kingdom, the plant kingdom). Kingdoms are then <u>subdivided</u> into smaller and smaller groups based on organisms' similarities and differences.

3) <u>Species</u> is the smallest group. Organisms of the same species, e.g. humans, are <u>closely-related</u> and can breed to produce <u>fertile offspring</u>.

4) The next smallest group is <u>genus</u> — a <u>genus</u> is a group of closely-related <u>species</u>. For example, in the genus '<u>canis</u>' there are domestic dogs, wild dogs, wolves and jackals.

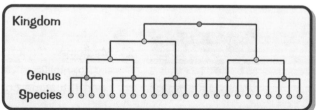

Not too keen on cells — they'll grow on you...

<u>Classification</u> started in the 1700s when a Swedish scientist Carolus Linnaeus decided he wanted order in life "for the greater glory of god." His work has made things <u>easier</u> for biologists today. With each species having a unique name there's little confusion about what animal is being studied.

Genes and Chromosomes

If you've ever wondered why animals or plants of the same species <u>look or behave slightly differently from</u> <u>each other</u> — you know, a bit <u>taller</u> or a bit <u>fatter</u> — well, it's partly due to their <u>genes</u>. All <u>animals</u> (including humans) are <u>different</u> from each other because their <u>genes</u> are slightly different. "But what is a gene?" I hear you cry. Well you're about to find out...

You Need to Know What Chromosomes and Genes Are

Whether you're talking about animals or plants, this basic stuff about genes is pretty much the same...

1) Nearly all <u>cells</u> have a <u>nucleus</u>. The nucleus contains a plant or animal's genetic information — this is what controls <u>everything</u> a cell does.

2) <u>Genetic information</u> is carried on long thread-like structures called <u>chromosomes</u>.

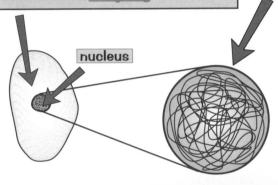

nucleus

3) When the cell divides, the chromosomes coil up into <u>X-shapes</u> (like the ones below). There are <u>two</u> of each chromosome in the nucleus — they come in <u>pairs</u>. The <u>human</u> cell nucleus contains <u>23 pairs</u> of chromosomes.

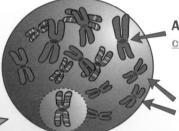

A single <u>chromosome</u>

4) Short sections of a chromosome are called <u>genes</u>. Genes control the characteristics of the body.

A <u>pair</u> of <u>chromosomes</u>

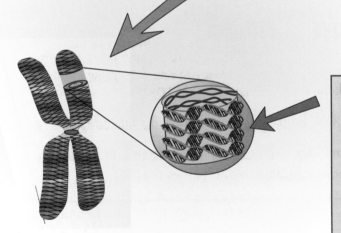

5) Genes contain <u>instructions</u> which tell cells what to do. Collectively they <u>determine how the organism functions</u>. So, genes determine your <u>characteristics</u> such as eye colour.

Genes — they always come in pairs...

This picture's true for <u>most</u> animals and plants (but the total number of chromosomes varies, and things like bacteria carry genetic information slightly differently). Genes are important, because genes control everything a cell <u>does</u>, as well as what <u>characteristics</u> parents pass on to their kids.

Variation

So, everyone in the world looks slightly different, partly because they've got slightly different genes. You might well be wondering why you have different genes... well... it's all down to a bit of 'how's your father'... nudge nudge, wink wink.

Genes are Inherited From Your Parents

1) The genes in the nucleus of your cells are a mixture of your parents' genes.

2) You inherit half from your dad and half from your mum.

3) So, why don't you look identical to your brother or sister? After all, they inherited their genes from the same mum and the same dad. Well, its all down to sexual reproduction — the way gametes (sperm and eggs cells) are formed and how they combine at fertilisation.

GAMETE FORMATION — MAKING SPERM CELLS AND EGG CELLS

1) Your reproductive cells, like your body cells, have two of each chromosome. In each pair there's one chromosome that was originally inherited from your mum, and one that was inherited from your dad.

2) To make gametes, reproductive cells split into two — when they do this the genes get shuffled up. Some of the genes from your dad are grouped with some from your mum.

3) The end result is gametes that contain only half the genetic material of normal cells — this type of cell division is called MEIOSIS.

4) This shuffling up of genetic material leads to variation in the next generation.

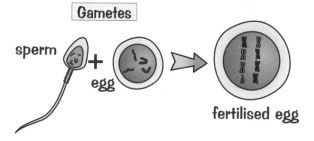

Gametes

sperm

+ egg

fertilised egg

FERTILISATION — JOINING TOGETHER THE GAMETES

1) Fertilisation is when the sperm and the egg, (both with half the normal number of chromosomes) join to form a new cell.

2) Any two gametes could join together, out of all the possible gametes. This creates even more variation.

The Fertilised Egg Grows by Mitosis

After all the shuffling of genes and the random selection of gametes, you get a mixture of genes that are totally individual. After that, the fertilised egg needs to grow into an adult. It does this through another type of cell division — MITOSIS.

Will you two stop cloning around

Mitosis is when a cell reproduces itself by dividing to form two identical cells.

1) A fertilised egg starts to grow by mitosis — repeatedly making copies of itself.

2) After a bit of this, these cells start to specialise into, e.g. nerve cells, blood cells, skin cells etc.

3) These different kinds of specialised cell then divide by mitosis again to create more specialised cells like themselves. All this division will lead to a baby and then (eventually) a fully-formed adult.

- Mitosis is responsible for all growth, and for repairing cells that have been damaged.

- When a cell is cloned it divides by mitosis. Cloning is the production of genetically identical cells or organisms. Scientists use cloning when they need lots of the same cell for research.

Well, I've said it all along — sex cells...

So in sexual reproduction a mixture of chromosomes is randomly shuffled into gametes. Then a random gamete fuses with another random gamete at fertilisation (oh, the romance of it all).

What Plants Need

Plants need food. Photosynthesis is the process that produces 'food' in plants. The 'food' it produces is glucose. Photosynthesis takes place in the leaves of all green plants — this is what leaves are for.

Photosynthesis Makes Glucose Using Sunlight

Photosynthesis uses energy from the Sun to convert carbon dioxide and water into glucose and oxygen. For photosynthesis to occur plants need:

1) Carbon dioxide — from the atmosphere, it enters through the leaves. The rate of photosynthesis can be increased by providing more CO_2.

2) Water — from the soil, enters through the roots.

3) Chlorophyll — the green substance found in chloroplasts (see page 34).

4) Light — (usually from the Sun) is needed to provide the energy for the reaction to occur. The rate of photosynthesis can be increased by providing more light and a higher temperature. Plants compete with each other for light. If lots of weeds grow in a field of crops, the weeds can block light from the crops, so the crops won't grow so well and crop yields are reduced.

Learn the word equation for photosynthesis:

$$\text{Carbon dioxide + Water} \xrightarrow[\text{chlorophyll}]{\text{LIGHT}} \text{Glucose + Oxygen}$$

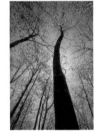

1) Glucose is a soluble sugar, it's transported (along with water) to the cells that need it.

2) If glucose isn't needed immediately it can be converted into STARCH (which is insoluble) and stored for times when it's in short supply, e.g. in winter.

Plants grow faster in the summer than they do in the winter because the days are longer (so there's more light) and it's warmer.

Respiration Uses Glucose to Provide Energy for the Plant

All living things need energy. Respiration is the process that releases energy from food. Plants use the glucose they produce during photosynthesis as their food source for respiration.

1) Plants release energy from glucose. So, any stored starch must first be broken down to glucose.

See p.47 for more on respiration in humans.

2) Respiration requires oxygen — plants get oxygen from the air through their leaves.

3) Water and carbon dioxide are produced as waste products.

The equation for respiration is the same as photosynthesis — just in the opposite direction:

$$\text{Glucose + Oxygen} \longrightarrow \text{Carbon dioxide + Water (+ Energy)}$$

Live and Learn...

It's not just poor GCSE students who need to learn about how plants photosynthesise. Farmers use this information to get the most out of their crops. Those that got stuck in at school know how to grow things like lettuce, tomatoes and even strawberries all year round — even in the UK's cold, dark, rubbish climate.

What Plants Need

As well as all the things plants needs for photosynthesis, they also need a whole host of minerals to grow healthily. Hmph, some things are just take, take, take, me, me, me.

Plants Need Minerals for Healthy Growth

1) In order to produce important compounds for healthy growth, plants need certain elements.
2) They get these elements from minerals in the soil.
3) Minerals in the soil are in solution (i.e. dissolved in water). The water containing the minerals is absorbed from the soil by the plant's roots.
4) If the plant can't get enough minerals it suffers deficiency symptoms.

Mineral Deficiency Stunts Growth

1) Nitrates

— these are needed to make proteins, which are needed for cell growth. If a plant can't get enough nitrates it will be stunted and will have yellow older leaves.

2) Phosphates

— they're needed for healthy growth, especially of roots. Plants without enough phosphate have poor root growth and purple older leaves.

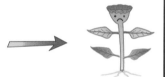

3) Potassium

— for healthy growth and flowering. If there's not enough potassium in the soil, plants have poor flower and fruit growth and discoloured leaves.

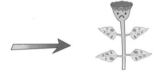

4) Magnesium (in smaller amounts)

— this is essential for making chlorophyll (needed for photosynthesis). Plants without enough magnesium have yellow leaves.

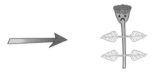

You might get a question about mineral deficiencies in your exam. They might ask you to interpret some data about plant growth in the presence or absence of minerals. Here's an example of what you might get:

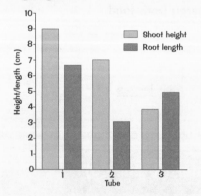

In this experiment seedlings were grown in three tubes. Tube one was the control, containing a complete mineral supply. The other tubes were deficient in either nitrates or phosphates. The exam question might ask you to identify which tube is deficient in which mineral. It's pretty easy really...

The control plant has good shoot and root growth. Tube two has good shoot growth but poor root growth. Tube three has poor shoot and root growth. We know that phosphate deficiency causes poor root growth so this must be tube two, and that nitrate deficiency causes general stunted growth — this must be tube three.

Where do plants get minerals from — a heath food store...

Plants can't always get all the minerals they need from the soil, so to help them along farmers can add fertilisers to their land — these can be artificial mixtures of the main minerals or manure. But farmers need to be careful when using them — careless use can be harmful to the environment (see page 41).

Intensive Farming

Farmers use what they know about plants to farm more <u>efficiently</u>, and with the world's <u>increasing</u> <u>population</u>, intensive farming could be just what we need — <u>bigger</u> and <u>better</u> yields.

Intensive Farming — Getting the Most Out of Plants and Animals

1) <u>Intensive farming</u> is where farmers try to get <u>as much as possible</u> from their plants and animals.

2) The aim is to produce the maximum amount of <u>food</u> from the <u>smallest possible</u> amount of <u>land</u>, to give a <u>huge variety</u> of <u>quality</u> foods, <u>all year round</u>, at <u>cheap prices</u>. They do this in <u>three</u> main ways...

1) Intensive Farming Uses Artificial Fertilisers...

1) Plants need <u>certain elements</u>, e.g. <u>nitrogen</u>, <u>potassium</u> and <u>phosphorus</u>, so they can make important compounds like proteins.

2) If plants don't get enough of these elements, their <u>growth</u> and <u>life processes</u> are affected (see the previous page).

3) Sometimes these elements are <u>missing</u> from the soil because they've been used up by a <u>previous crop</u>.

4) Farmers use artificial fertilisers to <u>replace</u> these missing elements or provide <u>more</u> of them. This helps to increase the <u>crop yield</u>.

2) ...As Well As Pesticides, Fungicides and Herbicides

1) <u>PESTICIDES</u> are chemicals that kill <u>farm pests</u>, e.g. insects, rats and mice. Pesticides that kill insects are called <u>insecticides</u>. Killing pests that would otherwise eat the crop means there's more left for us.

2) <u>FUNGICIDES</u> kill fungi, e.g. moulds that can damage crops.

3) <u>HERBICIDES</u> kill <u>weeds</u>. If you <u>remove</u> plants that compete for the same <u>resources</u>, e.g. nutrients from the soil, light (see page 37), it means the crop gets more of them and so grows better.

3) Animals can be Kept in Controlled Environments

1) In countries like the UK, animals such as <u>pigs</u> and <u>chickens</u> are often <u>intensively farmed</u> (battery farming).

2) They're kept <u>close together indoors</u> in small pens, so that they're <u>warm</u> and <u>can't move about</u>.

3) This saves them <u>wasting energy</u> on movement, and stops them giving out as much energy as <u>heat</u>.

4) This means the animals will <u>grow faster</u> on <u>less food</u>.

5) This makes things <u>cheaper</u> for the farmer, and for us when the animals finally turn up on supermarket shelves.

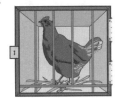

Intensive farming might just crop up in the exam...

The important stuff is knowing <u>how</u> intensive farming <u>increases</u> the amount of food — <u>fertilisers</u> provide essential <u>minerals</u> for growth. <u>Herbicides</u> remove <u>competition</u>, <u>pesticides</u> prevent diseases and putting animals in <u>controlled environments</u> means they <u>waste less energy</u> — all the more for us.

Organic Farming

Intensive farming methods are still used a lot. But people are also using organic methods more and more.

Organic Farming Doesn't Use Artificial Chemicals

An alternative to modern intensive farming is organic farming. Organic methods are more traditional. Where intensive farming uses chemical fertilisers, herbicides and pesticides, organic farming has more natural alternatives.

THE LAND IS KEPT FERTILE BY:

1) Using natural fertilisers (i.e. animal manure and compost). This recycles the nutrients left in plant and animal waste. It doesn't always work as well as artificial fertilisers, but it's better for the environment.

2) Crop rotation — growing a cycle of different crops in a field each year. This stops the pests and diseases of one crop building up, and means nutrients are less likely to run out (as each crop has different needs).

PESTS AND WEEDS ARE CONTROLLED BY:

1) Weeding — physically removing the weeds, rather than just spraying them with a herbicide. Obviously it takes a lot longer, but there are no nasty chemicals involved.

2) Varying crop growing times — farmers can avoid the major pests for a certain crop by planting it later or earlier in the season. This means they won't need pesticides.

3) Using natural pesticides — some pesticides are completely natural, and so long as they're used responsibly they don't mess up the ecosystem.

4) Biological control — Biological control means using a predator, a parasite or a disease to kill the pest, instead of chemicals. For example:

   a) Aphids are pests which eat roses and vegetables. Ladybirds are aphid predators, so people release them into their fields and gardens to keep aphid numbers down.

   b) Certain types of wasps and flies produce larvae which develop on (or in, yuck) a host insect. This eventually kills the host. Lots of insect pests have parasites like this.

   c) Myxomatosis is a disease that kills rabbits. In Australia the rabbit population grew out of control and ruined crops so the myxoma virus was released as a biological control.

Organic Farms Keep Animals in More Natural Conditions

1) For an animal farm to be classified as "organic", it has to follow guidelines on the ethical treatment of animals.

2) This means no battery farming — animals have to be free to roam outdoors for a certain number of hours every day.

3) Animals also have to be fed on organically-grown feed that doesn't contain any artificial chemicals.

Don't get bugged by biological pest control...

The Soil Association is an organisation that certifies farms fand products as organic. They have very strict rules about what products can carry their logo — much stricter than the Government's minimum standards. About 70% of all organic food sold in the UK is Soil Association approved.

Comparing Farming Methods

It's all very well knowing how the different farming methods work, but are they actually any good? Both intensive and organic methods have advantages and disadvantages, which I'm afraid you just have to learn.

Intensive Farming is Efficient but can Harm the Environment

The main advantage of intensive farming methods is that they produce large amounts of food in a very small space. But they can cause a few problems:

1) Lots of people think that intensive farming of animals such as battery hens is cruel.

2) The chemicals used can be damaging to the environment:

TOO MUCH FERTILISER — EUTROPHICATION

1) Problems start if some of the fertiliser finds its way into rivers and streams.

2) This happens quite easily if too much fertiliser is applied, especially if it rains afterwards.

3) The result is eutrophication, which can cause serious damage to rivers and lakes.

CHEMICALS DISTURB FOOD CHAINS

1) There's also a danger of chemicals (e.g. pesticides) passing through the food chain to other animals.

2) The diagram shows a food chain that ends with otters. The otter ends up with loads of the pesticide because it builds up at each level.

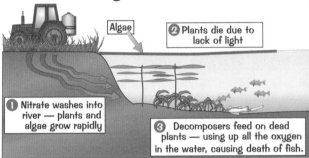

❶ Nitrate washes into river — plants and algae grow rapidly
Algae
❷ Plants die due to lack of light
❸ Decomposers feed on dead plants — using up all the oxygen in the water, causing death of fish.

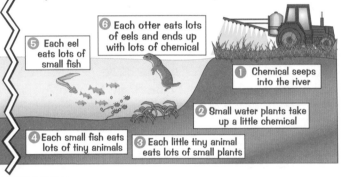

❻ Each otter eats lots of eels and ends up with lots of chemical
❺ Each eel eats lots of small fish
❶ Chemical seeps into the river
❷ Small water plants take up a little chemical
❹ Each small fish eats lots of tiny animals
❸ Each little tiny animal eats lots of small plants

TOO MUCH FERTILISER — NITRATES IN DRINKING WATER

1) Nitrate residues from excess fertiliser can also get into reservoirs.

2) If too many nitrates get into drinking water it can cause serious health problems, especially for young babies. Nitrates prevent the blood from carrying oxygen properly.

Organic Farming Has Advantages and Disadvantages Too

ADVANTAGES

1) Organic farming uses fewer chemicals, so there's less risk of toxic chemicals remaining on food.

2) It's better for the environment. There's less chance of polluting rivers with fertiliser. Organic farmers also avoid using pesticides, so they don't disrupt food chains and harm wildlife.

3) For a farm to be classed as organic, it will usually have to follow guidelines on the ethical treatment of animals. This means no battery farming.

DISADVANTAGES

1) Organic farming takes up more space than intensive farming — so more land has to be farmland, rather than being set aside for wildlife or for other uses.

2) It's more labour-intensive. This provides more jobs, but it also makes the food more expensive.

3) You can't grow as much food as you can with intensive farming — not as high productivity.

There's nowt wrong wi' spreadin' muck on it...

You need to be able to discuss the advantages and disadvantages of organic and intensive farming. If a question pops up in the exam don't just give your own opinions — its best to give both sides of the argument — even if you do happen to think battery farming is the best thing since sliced bread.

Food Chains and Webs

Everything in life is <u>linked together</u>, the smallest change in one species could have a <u>massive impact</u> on loads of others. That'll make you think twice next time you pull the legs off that poor defenceless spider.

Food Chains <u>Show</u> What <u>is</u> Eaten <u>by</u> What

Food chains show how <u>different organisms</u> are <u>dependent</u> on each other as <u>food sources</u>. They're made up of producers and consumers.

| <u>Producer</u>, e.g. carrot plants — <u>all plants</u> are producers. They get their energy from the <u>Sun</u>. | <u>Primary consumer</u>, e.g. rabbit — this is an animal that eats <u>producers</u> (plants). | <u>Secondary consumer</u>, e.g. fox — an animal that eats the <u>primary consumer</u>. |

1) In this <u>food chain</u> there are three different stages — these stages are called <u>trophic levels</u>.

2) Animals <u>eat</u> other organisms in a food chain and gain <u>energy</u> from those organisms. At each trophic level, there is a certain amount of energy available. The amount of <u>energy</u> available (and usually the <u>number</u> of organisms) <u>decreases</u> as you move <u>up</u> a <u>trophic level</u>.

3) You hardly ever get more than <u>five trophic levels</u> in a food chain. This is because so much <u>energy is lost</u> at each stage that there's <u>not enough</u> left to <u>support</u> more organisms after four or five stages.

Food Webs <u>Are Made Up Of Several</u> Food Chains...

<u>Food webs</u> show how <u>food chains are linked together</u>.

1) Each animal is <u>dependent</u> on the species it eats, e.g. the sparrow depends on the caterpillars for food.

2) If the <u>number</u> of one species <u>changes</u> it <u>affects all the others</u>. For example if all the caterpillars in an area died:

- There'd be <u>less food</u> for the <u>sparrows</u>, so their numbers would <u>decrease</u>.

- The number of <u>carrots</u> might <u>increase</u>, because there's no caterpillars to eat them.

- The <u>rabbits</u> would have <u>less competition</u> for food, so their numbers might increase.

3) But these are all just educated guesses, the actual <u>effects of change</u> in a food web are quite <u>unpredictable</u> — e.g. if the bird of prey couldn't eat caterpillars, it might <u>eat more rabbits</u> instead — causing the rabbit population to <u>decrease</u>, this would have a knock on effect on <u>foxes</u> etc.

Sausages — my favourite kind of food chain...

It's the job of <u>ecologists</u> is to study the <u>relationships</u> between <u>organisms</u>. Everything gets on quite well together if it's left <u>undisturbed</u> — the problem is food webs often get disturbed because of <u>changes in the environment</u>. These changes are often caused by us humans clomping about messing the place up. Typical.

Environmental Change

Lots of things we humans do affect the environment and the animals and plants that live in it.
Some organisms can cope with the changes we make to their homes but some aren't so fortunate.

Changing the Environment Affects Plants and Animals

Many of our modern day agricultural practices and industries have an impact on the environment and,
as a result, they affect all of the plants and animals which depend on the environment for their survival.

Intensive Farming Affects the Environment...

1) Excess fertiliser can have a massive impact on food chains and webs.
    Using chemicals (e.g. pesticides or herbicides) to remove an organism
    (the pest) from the environment means that you're removing the food
    another animal depends on. These chemicals can also accumulate in food
    chains, and can poison animals further up the food chain (see p.41).

2) Removing producers can also damage food chains and webs. When a crop is harvested the primary
    producer, the crop, is removed for us humans to eat. This means that other animals (usually the
    primary consumers) have a lot less to eat. This could have a knock-on effect on everything else
    in the food chain. But, this is the case in all types of farming, not only intensive farming.

...so does Burning Fossil Fuels

1) The burning of fossil fuels like coal, oil and natural gas releases
    carbon dioxide, which adds to the greenhouse effect (see p.112).

2) An increase in the greenhouse effect could lead to climate change.

3) Climate change could mean that some areas experience significant changes in
    temperature, rain fall and weather patterns. It could also cause flooding because of rising sea levels.

4) Changes in weather patterns could disrupt many of the natural processes of
    plants and animals, for example:

    • Flowering — a change in temperatures could change the flowering times of plants. Fruit and
      seeds may develop earlier in the year, and so won't be available when animals normally eat them.

    • Animal behaviour — a change in climate could affect migration patterns.
      E.g. birds may migrate to a regular breeding spot, but the climate there may have become
      unsuitable for breeding (e.g. too cold), forcing them to go somewhere else.

    • Distribution — plants and animals live in environments that they are the most suited to.
      If there is a significant change in climate their ideal environment may no longer exist.

Variation Helps Organisms Cope With Environmental Change

1) If all the different species couldn't adapt to new conditions, then environmental change could be
    disastrous and would probably wipe out many different species.

2) However, all organisms in a species are slightly different because of their genes (see p.35) — these
    differences are called variation. So if a population's environment changes, e.g. becomes hotter or
    more polluted, there will be some individuals that can cope with the change because of variation.

3) Many individuals in the population will be affected by the change, but those with the ability to cope
    will survive. They will pass on the trait which allows them to cope to their offspring.

4) The trait that allows them to survive in the new environment will then be common in the population.

Variation is the spice of life...

Polar bears are already being affected by a change in climate. They live on sea ice in the Arctic, hunting
seals. But as the Arctic temperature has increased the sea ice melts earlier than usual — giving them
less time to hunt for food. So, the survival of the polar bear is uncertain. Let's hope they can adapt.

Selective Breeding

'Selective breeding' sounds like it has the potential to be a tricky topic, but it's actually dead simple. You take the <u>best</u> plants or animals and breed them together to get the best possible <u>offspring</u>. That's it.

Selective Breeding _is Very Simple_

<u>Selective breeding</u> is where we select the plants or animals that are going to <u>breed</u> according to what <u>we</u> want from them. This means that the desirable genes will remain in the population. This is the basic process involved in <u>selective breeding</u>:

1) From your existing stock, <u>select</u> the ones which have the <u>best characteristics</u>.

   The characteristics that are considered the 'best' will vary, but it usually means things like:
   - <u>Maximum yield</u> of meat, milk, grain etc.
   - <u>Good health</u> and <u>disease resistance</u>.
   - Qualities like <u>temperament</u>, <u>speed</u>, <u>fertility</u> and <u>good mothering skills</u>, for animals.
   - Qualities like <u>attractive flowers</u>, <u>nice smell</u> and <u>high yield</u> for plants.

2) <u>Breed them</u> with each other (this is sometimes called <u>cross breeding</u>).
3) Select the <u>best</u> of the <u>offspring</u>, and <u>breed them together</u>.
4) This process is continued over <u>several generations</u>, to develop the desired trait.

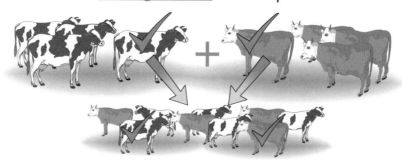

The Main Drawback _is a_ Reduction _in the_ Gene Pool

1) The main problem with selective breeding is that it reduces the <u>genetic variation</u> in a population. Because the farmer keeps breeding from the <u>same plants or animals</u> — the "<u>best</u>" ones — all the animals in a population are genetically very similar.

2) There's more chance of the organisms developing <u>genetic diseases</u>.
3) There can also be problems if a <u>new disease appears</u> because there's <u>little variety</u> in the population.
   All the stock are <u>closely related</u> to each other, so if one of them is going to be killed by a new disease, the others are <u>also</u> likely to succumb to it.

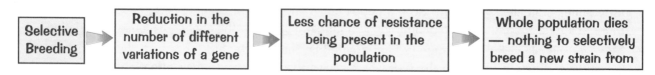

| Selective Breeding | → | Reduction in the number of different variations of a gene | → | Less chance of resistance being present in the population | → | Whole population dies — nothing to selectively breed a new strain from |

I use the same genes all the time too — they flatter my hips...

Selective breeding's <u>not</u> a <u>new</u> thing. People have been doing it for yonks. That's how we ended up with something like a <u>poodle</u> from a <u>wolf</u>. Somebody thought 'I really like this small, woolly, yappy wolf — I'll breed it with this other one'. And after <u>thousands of generations</u>, we got poodles. Hurrah.

Genetic Engineering

Selective breeding is okay, but it can take quite a while (you have to wait for the cows to squeeze out little calves) and even then it's all a bit random. Never fear, scientists have another idea...

Genes Can be Transferred into Different Organisms

Selective breeding has been used for years by farmers. Scientists have now come up with a more efficient way of producing organisms with all the desired traits — genetic engineering.

1) Genetic engineering is where genes are transferred from one organism to another.

2) 'Foreign' genes (ones from another organism) can be transferred into plant or animal cells or into microorganisms.

3) The characteristics that the plant or animal displays depends on the type of gene inserted — the possibilities are endless.

1) Long-life tomatoes can be made by changing the gene that causes fruit to ripen. This could be done with lots of other fruit and vegetables.

2) Animals can be modified to be bigger or grow quicker — increasing meat yield. We already have the technology to do this in salmon.

3) Crops with added vitamins or minerals. A rice enhanced with vitamin A — called golden rice, has already been produced.

Genetic Engineering Has Advantages and Risks

It's a young science with exciting possibilities — but there's also potential dangers. You need to be able to explain some of the advantages and risks involved in genetic engineering.

1) The main advantage is that you can produce organisms with new and very useful features (like those mentioned above). They have the potential to help lots of people.

2) The main risk is that the inserted gene could have unexpected harmful effects. Genes are often inserted into bacteria. The bacteria could mutate and become pathogenic (disease causing). People also worry about the engineered DNA 'escaping' — e.g. crops can be engineered to be herbicide resistant but if these genes passed into a weed then they'd be unstoppable.

Genetic Engineering Has Moral and Ethical Issues

1) Some people think it's wrong to genetically engineer other organisms purely for human benefit. This is a particular problem in the genetic engineering of animals, especially if the animal suffers as a result.

2) People worry that we won't stop at engineering plants and animals. Those who can afford it might decide which characteristics they want their children to have, creating a 'genetic underclass'.

3) There are also concerns about 'playing God', and meddling with things that should be left well alone.

4) The long-term evolutionary consequences of genetic engineering are unknown, but there could potentially be quite a few, e.g. seedless fruit — it's seedless so never reproduces sexually, which means that it won't evolve and can't change with the surrounding environment.

Barry played god in the school nativity — I was a sheep...

The possibilities really are endless, I'd like to put the genes of a spider into a giant rat and add a few ninja genes — just for luck. I'd have my own army of giant ninja spider rats, no one could stop me then, I'd take over the world. Mwa ha ha ha ha... actually... maybe not.

Revision Summary for Section 2.1

Phew. That was a pretty tough section, covering lots of facts, processes, view-points and issues. You've covered loads of things to do with living organisms and how we can use them to our advantage. It's all pretty interesting and relevant to things happening today. As a reward, here are some nice questions I prepared earlier...

1) State the word equation for fermentation in yeast.
2) What is an enzyme?
3) What makes bread rise?
4) What does fermentation in bacteria produce?
5) What conditions are needed for fermentation?
6) Name three useful products from plants.
7) Name three useful products from animals.
8) Where in a cell is the genetic material found?
9) Give three differences between plant and animal cells.
10) How are organisms classified into groups?
11) What is a gene?
12) What is meiosis?
13) How is variation created in gamete formation?
14) What is mitosis?
15) What four things do plants need in order to carry out photosynthesis?
16) State the word equation for photosynthesis.
17) How can you increase the rate of photosynthesis?
18) How is the glucose produced by photosynthesis used to provide energy to the plant?
19) How do minerals enter a plant?
20) Which mineral is needed for flowering?
21) What do plants use magnesium for?
22) Why do farmers use artificial fertilisers?
23) Why do farmers use herbicides?
24) Why is it cheaper to keep animals in a controlled environment?
25) Give an example of a natural fertiliser.
26) Describe how biological control reduces pests in organic farming.
27) Give two disadvantages of intensive farming.
28) Give two disadvantages of organic farming.
29) Why do you rarely get more than five trophic levels in a food chain?
30) Describe how intensive farming can change the environment.
31) Give an example of how changes in the environment affect animals.
32) Why do people selectively breed livestock?
33) What is the main drawback of selective breeding?
34) What is the main risk of genetic engineering?
35) Give two moral or ethical issues of genetic engineering.

Respiration

By knowing all about <u>how</u> the body functions, <u>doctors</u> can help treat people when things <u>go wrong</u>. <u>Sports' scientists</u> learn all this stuff too so they can help <u>improve athletes' performance</u>. Respiration is a <u>really important process</u> in the body — it <u>releases</u> the <u>energy</u> we need from all that <u>food</u> we eat. Without respiration you wouldn't be able to live, let alone revise.

Respiration is <u>NOT</u> "breathing in and out"

1) Respiration is <u>NOT</u> breathing in and breathing out, as you might think.

2) <u>Respiration</u> actually goes on in <u>every cell</u> in your body.

3) It's the process of releasing <u>energy</u> from <u>glucose</u> (i.e. from sugar in your food).

4) This energy is then used to do things like:

See page 49 for breathing in and out.

Build up <u>larger molecules</u> (like proteins).

Contract <u>muscles</u>.

Maintain a steady <u>body temperature</u>.

5) All living things '<u>respire</u>', including plants. The big difference between us and plants is that they <u>make</u> their own glucose (using light, see page 37) and we get ours from the food we eat.

6) Here's a nice <u>definition</u> of respiration for you...

> **RESPIRATION is the process of RELEASING ENERGY from GLUCOSE, which goes on IN EVERY CELL.**

7) The <u>sugar</u> actually <u>reacts</u> with <u>oxygen</u> in the cells. Here's the word <u>equation</u>:

> Glucose + Oxygen → Carbon Dioxide + Water (+ Energy)

So, For Respiration Your <u>Cells</u> Need <u>Glucose</u>...

1 The sugary <u>food</u> you eat is <u>digested</u> into <u>glucose</u> and <u>moves</u> from the <u>digestive system</u> into the <u>blood</u>.

2 The <u>blood</u> then <u>carries</u> <u>glucose</u> to the <u>cells</u>.

... And <u>Oxygen</u>

1 Breathing in moves <u>oxygen</u> into your <u>lungs</u> (see page 49).

2 <u>Oxygen</u> then <u>moves</u> into your <u>blood</u> (see page 50).

3 <u>Blood</u> moves around the <u>circulatory system</u> (see page 52) to all <u>cells</u>, <u>supplying</u> the oxygen they need for <u>respiration</u>.

People say I'm greedy — I just eat out of respiration...

Isn't it strange to think that <u>each individual living cell</u> in your body is <u>respiring</u> every <u>second</u> of every <u>day</u> releasing energy from the food you eat. Next time someone accuses you of being lazy you could claim that you're busy respiring — it's enough to make anyone feel tired.

Energy for Exercise

The <u>more exercise</u> you do, the <u>more you need to respire</u> to keep all your muscle cells supplied with the energy they need. Sometimes the body can't get enough oxygen, but fear not — it has <u>clever way of coping</u> that allows you to continue exercising while keeping all those little cells happy.

When You *Exercise* You *Respire More*

1) As you've seen, your body gets <u>energy</u> from <u>respiration</u> — sugar reacts with oxygen in your cells to release the energy that you need.

2) Muscles need <u>energy</u> from respiration to <u>contract</u>.

3) When you exercise some of your muscles contract <u>more frequently</u> than normal so you need <u>more energy</u>.

4) This energy comes from <u>increased respiration</u>.

5) The increase in respiration means you need to get <u>more oxygen</u> and glucose into the cells. So...

- Your <u>breathing rate increases</u> to get more oxygen into the blood.
- Your <u>heart rate increases</u> to get glucose and oxygenated blood around the body to your muscles quicker (this removes CO_2 quickly at the same time).

6) But, when you do <u>really vigorous exercise</u> (like sprinting) your body can't supply <u>oxygen</u> to your muscles <u>quickly enough</u> — they start using a different type of respiration called <u>anaerobic respiration</u>.

Anaerobic *Respiration* Doesn't *Use Oxygen At All*

1) <u>Anaerobic respiration</u> happens when there's <u>not enough oxygen available</u>.

2) <u>Anaerobic</u> just means <u>without air</u> and it's <u>NOT the best way to release energy from glucose</u>.

You need to learn the <u>word equation</u>:

$$\text{Glucose} \rightarrow \text{Lactic Acid} \ (+ \text{ Energy})$$

3) <u>Anaerobic respiration</u> doesn't <u>release</u> nearly as much <u>energy</u> as aerobic respiration — but it's useful for short bursts of exercise.

Step classes underwater — anaerobics...

Isn't <u>exercise</u> just great, I love it. Pushing yourself that little bit harder, feeling the burn. Losing half your body weight in sweat. Running so far you vomit and even cry a little bit, oh you can't beat it. The aches and pains soon disappear, once you've had a nice little sit down, and some cake that is.

The Respiratory System: Breathing

You need to get air (containing <u>oxygen</u>) into your lungs so the oxygen can move into the blood... which is where <u>breathing</u> comes in. (They sometimes call it '<u>ventilation</u>' in the exams — don't get confused with those big shiny metal things that Bruce Willis likes climbing through, it's just breathing, OK.)
The <u>respiratory system</u> is responsible for controlling breathing.

The Respiratory System is in the Top Part of Your Body

There are a few parts you need to know...

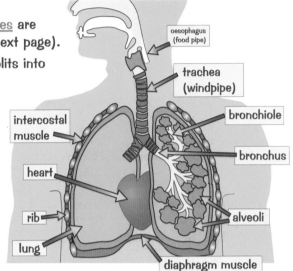

1) The <u>lungs</u> are like big pink <u>sponges</u>. This is where <u>gases</u> are <u>exchanged</u> (move into and out of the blood, see the next page).

2) The <u>trachea</u> (the pipe from the mouth to the lungs) splits into two tubes called '<u>bronchi</u>' — one goes to each lung.

3) The bronchi split into progressively smaller tubes called <u>bronchioles</u> that end with small bags called <u>alveoli</u> — this is where gas exchange takes place.

4) The <u>ribs</u> protect the lungs and the heart. They're also important in breathing (see below).

5) The <u>intercostal muscles</u> are the muscles in between the ribs.

6) The <u>diaphragm</u> is the large muscle at the bottom of the lungs — it's also important for breathing.

Breathing In and Out Uses Muscles

The <u>diaphragm</u> and <u>intercostal muscles</u> play an important role in breathing in (<u>inhaling</u>) and out (<u>exhaling</u>).

Breathing In...

1) <u>Intercostals</u> and <u>diaphragm contract</u>.
2) <u>Ribcage</u> moves <u>up</u> and <u>out</u>.
3) Thorax volume <u>increases</u>.
4) This draws air <u>in</u>.

...and Breathing Out

1) <u>Intercostals</u> and <u>diaphragm relax</u>.
2) <u>Ribcage</u> drops <u>down</u> and <u>in</u>.
3) Thorax volume <u>decreases</u>.
4) Air is forced <u>out</u>.

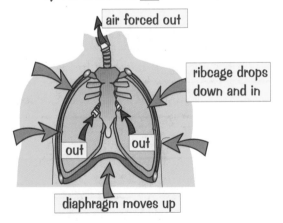

Stop huffing and puffing and just LEARN IT...

If you've ever fancied a career in the <u>medical profession</u> then you'll need to know this stuff inside out. Plus it comes in really handy in everyday life — I regularly drop interesting biology facts into conversation in an attempt to woo the opposite sex. Even if it doesn't go down too well at least it's stuck in your head that air is drawn <u>into the lungs</u> when the intercostals and diaphragm <u>contract</u>. Oh, and it'll also be useful in the exam. So many reasons to learn this page.

The Respiratory System: Gas Exchange

How to get <u>air into</u> the <u>lungs</u> is just the start, a little something to whet your appetite. How this air in your lungs gets to <u>every single little cell in your body</u> — now that's where the real fun is. Bet you can't wait.

Gas Exchange *Takes Place in the* Alveoli...

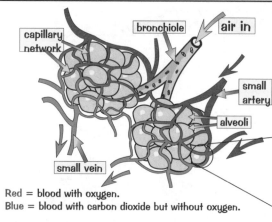

Red = blood with oxygen.
Blue = blood with carbon dioxide but without oxygen.

1) The job of the lungs is to transfer <u>oxygen into</u> the <u>blood</u> and to <u>remove carbon dioxide</u> from it.

2) To do this the lungs contain millions of <u>alveoli</u> where <u>gas exchange</u> takes place.

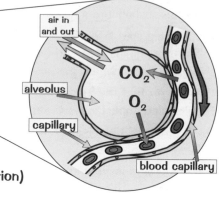

3) <u>Oxygen</u> passes out of the alveolus and into the capillary (see p.52) and is taken up by the <u>red blood cells</u> (see p.51).

4) At the same time <u>carbon dioxide</u> (the waste product of respiration) passes <u>out of the blood</u> and back into the <u>lungs</u> to be exhaled.

...*and at the* Cells

1) When the blood reaches the <u>cells</u>, <u>oxygen</u> is released from the red blood cells and <u>moves into</u> the <u>body cells</u> (for respiration).

2) At the same time, <u>carbon dioxide</u> produced by respiration <u>moves into</u> the <u>blood</u> to be carried back to the lungs. Carbon dioxide has to be <u>removed</u> from the body as it's <u>toxic</u>.

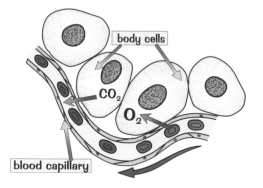

The Composition of Inhaled and Exhaled *Air is Different*

The air you <u>breathe out</u> is different to the air you <u>breathe in</u>:

Component	Inhaled air	Exhaled air
Nitrogen	79%	79%
Oxygen	21%	17%
Carbon Dioxide	0%	4%

The percentage of <u>nitrogen doesn't change</u> as it's not used by the body.

The percentage of <u>oxygen</u> is <u>lower</u> in <u>exhaled air</u> because some of it has <u>moved</u> into the <u>blood</u>.

The percentage of <u>carbon dioxide</u> is <u>higher</u> in <u>exhaled air</u> because it's <u>produced</u> in respiration and passes from the blood to the lungs.

The amount of <u>moisture</u> is <u>higher</u> in <u>exhaled</u> air than inhaled air. The exhaled air will also be <u>warmer</u>.

Alveoli con granchio — my favourite pasta dish...

Alveoli are really <u>important</u> but they can be <u>damaged</u> really <u>easily</u>. There's a lung condition called <u>emphysema</u> where the alveoli are damaged — this affects <u>gas exchange</u> and makes it really hard to get enough oxygen into the body. Emphysema can be caused by <u>smoking</u> — kids, don't smoke or else.

The Circulatory System: Blood

Blood — it's very useful stuff. Its main use is to make you look cool when you fall off your bike, but it's also pretty good at carrying things around the body...

Blood is a Fluid Made Up of Four Main Things

The blood is basically a big transport system for moving substances to and from body cells. Its main jobs are:

- To transport oxygen and food to cells for respiration.
- To remove waste products, e.g. carbon dioxide (from respiration).
- To help fight off microorganisms.
- To stop you bleeding too much when you cut yourself.

You need to learn the four main bits that help it do this:

1) Red Blood Cells Carry Oxygen

The job of the red blood cells is to transport oxygen from the lungs to all the cells in the body.

1) Red blood cells contain a substance that can carry oxygen.
2) At the lungs red blood cells pick up oxygen.
3) At the body cells the red blood cells then release oxygen.

2) White Blood Cells Fight Disease

1) White blood cells play a really important role in protecting your body against attack from microorganisms.
2) They travel around the blood and crawl into every part of you, constantly patrolling for microorganisms. When they come across an invading microorganism they engulf it (see page 60).

3) Platelets Help Blood Clot

1) Platelets are small fragments of cells.
2) They help the blood to clot at the site of a wound. This stops all your blood pouring out and stops microorganisms getting in. (So basically they just float about waiting for accidents to happen!)

4) Plasma is the Liquid Bit

Plasma is a pale yellow liquid which carries just about everything:

mmm... plasma

1) Red blood cells, white blood cells and platelets.
2) Water.
3) Waste products, e.g. carbon dioxide from the body cells to the lungs.
4) Digested food products like glucose. These are absorbed from the gut and taken to the body cells.
5) Hormones — these act as chemical messengers (see page 55).

Platelets — good for small dinners...

And you thought blood was just red and wet — turns out there's a lot more to it. It's important not just to learn what the different parts of blood are — also make sure you know what they all do.

The Circulatory System: The Heart

Blood doesn't just move around the body <u>on its own</u>, of course. It needs a <u>pump</u>.

The <u>Heart Pumps Blood</u> <u>Around the</u> <u>Circulatory System</u>

1) The heart is a <u>pump</u> — it supplies the force to move blood around your body through <u>blood vessels</u>. To every last tissue and back.

2) Mammals have a <u>double circulatory system</u> — this means that there are <u>two circuits</u> joined together.

3) The first one connects the <u>heart</u> to the <u>lungs</u>. <u>Deoxygenated</u> blood (blood without oxygen) is pumped to the <u>lungs</u> to take in <u>oxygen</u>. The blood then <u>returns</u> to the heart.

4) The second one pumps the <u>oxygenated</u> blood around the <u>body</u>. The blood <u>gives up</u> its oxygen at the body cells, and the <u>deoxygenated</u> blood <u>returns</u> to the heart to be pumped out to the <u>lungs</u> again.

5) The blood is carried around the body in <u>blood vessels</u>. There are three types:

> <u>Arteries</u> — transport blood <u>away</u> from the heart.
>
> <u>Veins</u> — transport blood <u>to</u> the heart.
>
> <u>Capillaries</u> — these small blood vessels <u>link</u> the arteries and veins and are where <u>materials</u> are <u>exchanged</u> with the cells, e.g. oxygen and carbon dioxide.

Lungs

Rest of Body

<u>Learn</u> <u>**This**</u> <u>Diagram</u> <u>of the</u> <u>Heart</u> <u>with All Its</u> <u>Labels</u>

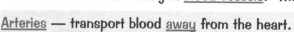

Right Side   Left Side

to body

to lungs

from body

from lungs

right atrium

left atrium

semilunar valve

semilunar valve

bicuspid valve

tricuspid valve

right ventricle

left ventricle

(No, we haven't got our left and right muddled up — this is the left and right side of the person whose heart it is, your left is their right, like looking in a mirror)

1) The <u>right atrium</u> of the heart receives <u>deoxygenated</u> blood from the <u>body</u>.

2) The deoxygenated blood moves through to the <u>right ventricle</u>, which pumps it to the <u>lungs</u>.

3) The <u>left atrium</u> receives <u>oxygenated</u> blood from the <u>lungs</u>.

4) The oxygenated blood then moves through to the <u>left ventricle</u>, which pumps it out round the <u>whole body</u>.

5) The <u>semilunar</u>, <u>tricuspid</u> and <u>bicuspid valves</u> prevent the <u>backflow</u> of blood.

<u>Okay — let's get to the heart of the matter...</u>

The human heart beats <u>100 000 times a day</u> on average. You can feel a pulse in your wrist or neck (where the vessels are close to the surface). This is the <u>blood</u> being pushed along by another beat. Doctors use a <u>stethoscope</u> to listen to your heart — it's actually the <u>valves closing</u> that they hear. Cool.

The Nervous System

Your environment is constantly changing and your body must be able to <u>respond</u> to these changes. The job of the nervous system is to send <u>information</u> around the body about any <u>changes</u>.

Sense Organs **Contain** Receptors **That** Detect Stimuli

<u>Receptors</u> are groups of cells that are sensitive to a <u>stimulus</u> such as light or heat, etc. There are five different <u>sense organs</u>, which all contain different <u>receptors</u>.

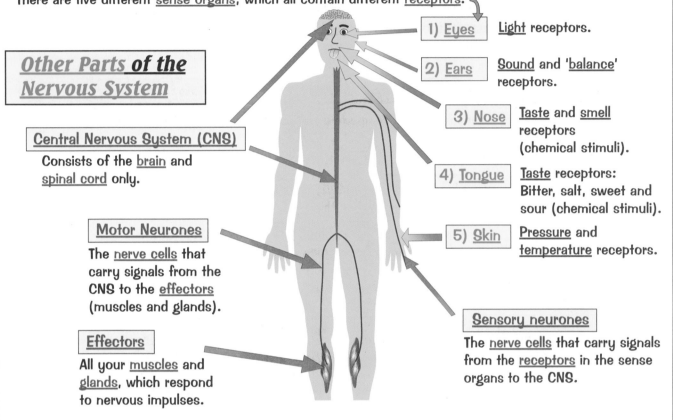

1) <u>Eyes</u>   <u>Light</u> receptors.

2) <u>Ears</u>   <u>Sound</u> and '<u>balance</u>' receptors.

3) <u>Nose</u>   <u>Taste</u> and <u>smell</u> receptors (chemical stimuli).

4) <u>Tongue</u>   <u>Taste</u> receptors: Bitter, salt, sweet and sour (chemical stimuli).

5) <u>Skin</u>   <u>Pressure</u> and <u>temperature</u> receptors.

Other Parts **of the** Nervous System

Central Nervous System (CNS)

Consists of the <u>brain</u> and <u>spinal cord</u> only.

Motor Neurones

The <u>nerve cells</u> that carry signals from the CNS to the <u>effectors</u> (muscles and glands).

Effectors

All your <u>muscles</u> and <u>glands</u>, which respond to nervous impulses.

Sensory neurones

The <u>nerve cells</u> that carry signals from the <u>receptors</u> in the sense organs to the CNS.

The Central Nervous System **(CNS)** Coordinates **Information**

The nervous system uses nerves to <u>communicate</u> information <u>quickly</u> all around the body.

Here's what happens:

1) A stimulus is <u>detected</u> by receptors in a sense organ.

2) This information travels along <u>sensory neurones</u> to the CNS.

3) The CNS is like the <u>control centre</u> of your nervous system. Its job is to **COORDINATE** all the information and <u>decide</u> what <u>needs to be done</u>.

4) The CNS will send information to the relevant <u>effector</u> (muscle or gland) along <u>motor neurones</u>. The effector will then <u>respond accordingly</u>.

EXAMPLE You're having fish and chips at the seaside and a hungry seagull fancies one of your chips and starts flying at you. Luckily, the <u>light receptors</u> in your eyes detect the incoming gull. Your eyes then send a <u>signal</u> to your <u>CNS via sensory neurones</u>. The CNS <u>processes</u> the information and decides that it'd be a good idea to <u>move your chips</u> so the seagull can't get them. So, your CNS sends a signal via the <u>motor neurones</u> to the effectors — the <u>muscles</u> in your arm and shoulder. They contract and your chips are safely tucked away. Phew.

Hurrah for sense organs — without them you couldn't revise...

Well, maybe not hurrah then. In a <u>single cubic centimetre</u> of your <u>brain</u> you can have well <u>over 50 million</u> nerve cells. Each one of these exciting little cells can communicate with <u>thousands</u> of other nerve cells to process information from the <u>receptors</u> — and you thought computers were impressive.

Maintaining Constant Temperature

Your nervous system also constantly monitors your internal environment (your insides) to make sure everything's working properly and you have the right body temperature...

The Nervous System Helps to Keep Body Temperature Constant

1) The reactions in your body (e.g. respiration — see p.47) work best at about 37 °C.

2) This means that you need to keep your body temperature around this value — within 1 or 2 °C of it.

3) A part of your brain acts as your own personal thermostat. So it's your nervous system that controls your body temperature (see previous page for more about the nervous system).

The Skin has a Nifty Trick for Altering Body Temperature

When the brain senses changes in the body temperature it sends nervous impulses to the skin.

When You're TOO HOT:

~ You might also sweat and find somewhere cool, e.g. in the shade. ~

1) Blood vessels (see p.52) close to the skin's surface get bigger in diameter — this is called vasodilation.

2) This means that more blood gets to the surface of the skin. The warm blood then loses some of its heat to the surroundings. (This is why you look red when you're hot — it's the increased blood flow to the surface of the skin.)

Blood vessels close to the skin's surface get bigger in diameter

When You're TOO COLD:

~ You also shiver to try and warm yourself up. ~

1) Blood vessels close to the skin's surface get smaller in diameter — this is called vasoconstriction.

2) This means that less blood gets to the surface of the skin, which stops the blood losing its heat to the surroundings. (This is why you look paler when you're really cold — there's very little blood going to the surface of the skin.)

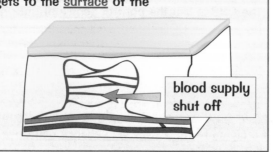

blood supply shut off

Sweaty and red — I'm so attractive in the heat...

If you get way too hot you could get heat exhaustion — you feel really tired and a bit sick, and if it's untreated you could die... scary. It's a similar story if you get too cold (the fancy name for this is hypothermia) — you can slip into a coma and die. Also, getting too cold isn't great for your fingers, toes and nose — if the blood supply is cut off for too long the cells in the tissues die. This causes frostbite (where the fingers and toes go all black and manky) and it's quite common in mountaineers.

Hormones and Blood Sugar

Hormones aren't just pesky chemicals that make you an awkward teenager — whatever your mother might say. They're actually <u>very useful little things</u> that help your body <u>run like clockwork</u> every single day — they're another way to <u>communicate information</u> around the body.

Hormones are Chemical Messengers Sent in the Blood

1) Hormones are chemicals produced in various <u>glands</u>. The glands release hormones directly into the <u>blood</u>. The blood then carries the hormones all over the body. They only affect <u>particular cells</u> in particular organs, called <u>target cells</u>. Their <u>response</u> is <u>slower</u> than a response carried by nerves because they travel at "<u>the speed of blood</u>".

2) Hormones cause <u>slow changes</u> within the body, e.g. they control <u>growth</u> and <u>development</u>.

Insulin is a Hormone that Controls Blood Sugar Levels

Insulin is a hormone produced by the <u>pancreas</u> that helps control the level of sugar in your blood...

1) Eating <u>carbohydrate</u> foods puts a lot of <u>glucose</u> into the blood from the <u>gut</u>.

2) The normal working of cells (i.e. respiration) <u>removes</u> glucose from the blood.

3) Vigorous <u>exercise</u> removes loads of glucose from the blood.

4) Obviously, to keep the <u>level</u> of blood glucose <u>controlled</u> there has to be a way to <u>add or remove</u> glucose from the blood. And this is it:

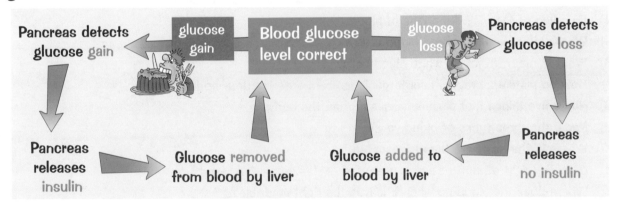

Remember, the <u>addition</u> of insulin <u>reduces</u> blood sugar level.

Diabetes — the Pancreas Stops Making Enough Insulin

1) <u>Diabetes</u> (type 1) is a disorder where the <u>pancreas</u> doesn't produce enough <u>insulin</u>.

2) The result is that a person's blood sugar can rise to a level that can <u>kill them</u>.

3) The problem can be <u>controlled</u> in <u>two ways</u>:

a) <u>Avoiding foods</u> rich in <u>carbohydrate</u> (which is broken down into glucose when digested).

b) <u>Injecting insulin</u> into the blood before meals (especially if high in sugars). This <u>removes</u> the <u>glucose</u> from the blood as soon as it enters it from the gut, when the (carbohydrate-rich) food is being <u>digested</u>. This stops the level of glucose in the blood from getting too high and is a very effective treatment. However, the person must make sure they <u>eat sensibly</u> after injecting insulin, or their blood sugar could <u>drop dangerously</u>.

My blood sugar feels low after that — pass the biscuits...

Diabetics can <u>check</u> their blood sugar using a <u>glucose-monitoring device</u>. This is a little hand-held machine. They prick their finger to get a drop of <u>blood</u> for the machine to check. Handy.

Revision Summary 1 for Section 2.2

¡Hola! y bienvenido a Quién quiere ser millonario. Responda correctamente a quince preguntas y usted podría volver a casa con un millón de euros. Juguemos. Oh hang on, wait a minute, I forgot I'm not presenting the Spanish Who Wants To Be A Millionaire any more, sorry. Oh how the mighty have fallen. You don't have any lifelines, and the chances of winning a million by answering these questions are mighty slim, but why not give them a go anyway.

1) Where does respiration occur?

2) What substance does respiration release energy from?

3) Give the word equation for respiration.

4) What is the energy released in respiration used for?

5) During exercise, how do oxygen and glucose get to your muscles faster?

6) In humans, when does anaerobic respiration occur?

7) Give the word equation for anaerobic respiration.

8) Sketch a diagram of the thorax and label the parts of the respiratory system.

9) Name the two muscles involved in breathing in and out.

10) Which gas is produced as a waste product of respiration?

11) Why does this gas have to be removed from the body?

12) Approximately what percentage of a) inhaled air and b) exhaled air is nitrogen?

13) Describe how the compositions of inhaled and exhaled air are different.

14) Give two of the main functions of blood.

15) What is the main job of red blood cells?

16) What is the main job of white blood cells?

17) How do platelets prevent microorganisms from entering your body?

18) Name five things that plasma carries around the body.

19) Name the three types of blood vessel.

20) Where in the heart are the atria located?

21) Does the right atrium receive oxygenated or deoxygenated blood?

22) Where does the blood go when it leaves the right ventricle?

23) What is the function of the valves in the heart?

24) List the five sense organs.

25) Where do motor neurones carry signals to?

26) Name the two organs that make up the central nervous system.

27) What is the function of the central nervous system?

28) What is the ideal human body temperature?

29) What controls your body temperature?

30) How does vasodilation help you cool down?

31) How does vasoconstriction help keep you warm?

32) Name two processes that hormones control.

33) Where is insulin produced?

34) What is diabetes?

35) Give two ways in which diabetes can be controlled.

Infectious Disease

Microorganisms are organisms that are <u>microscopic</u> (unsurprisingly). There are 'good' ones and there are 'bad' ones, which cause <u>horrid diseases</u> that make you <u>really ill</u> (there are even some ugly ones).

Infectious Diseases are Caused by Pathogens

1) <u>Pathogens</u> are <u>microorganisms</u> that cause <u>disease</u>.
2) Human pathogens can <u>reproduce very fast</u> inside the <u>body</u> — they love the <u>warm conditions</u>.
3) Pathogens include some <u>bacteria</u>, some <u>fungi</u> and <u>all viruses</u>. Here's a bit more about them:

1) Bacteria are Very Small Living Cells

1) Bacteria are <u>very small cells</u> (about 1/100th the size of your body cells) that can reproduce rapidly inside your body.
2) They can make you <u>feel ill</u> by <u>damaging your cells</u> and by <u>producing toxins</u> (poisons).
3) Bacteria can cause diseases like:

Bacteria are cells with no nucleus. The genetic material is free in the cell.

> <u>Tuberculosis</u> — a <u>lung</u> infection.
>
> <u>Meningitis</u> — <u>swelling of tissue</u> around the <u>brain</u>.
>
> <u>Pneumonia</u> — a <u>lung</u> infection.
>
> (Meningitis and pneumonia are both caused by the bacterium *Staphylococcus aureus*.)

Some bacteria are <u>useful</u> if they're in the <u>right place</u>, like in your digestive system.

2) Viruses aren't Cells — They're Much Smaller

1) Viruses are <u>not cells</u>. They're <u>tiny</u>, about 1/100th the size of a bacterium. They're usually no more than a <u>coat of protein</u> around their <u>genetic material</u>.
2) They <u>replicate</u> by <u>invading</u> cells and using the cells to produce many <u>copies</u> of themselves. The cell will usually then <u>burst</u>, releasing all the new viruses. This <u>cell damage</u> is what makes you feel ill.

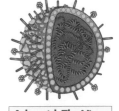

A horrid Flu Virus

3) Viruses can cause diseases like:

> <u>Measles</u> — a disease that causes <u>fever</u> and a <u>distinctive rash</u>.
>
> <u>Mumps</u> — an infection of the <u>salivary glands</u>.
>
> <u>Rubella</u> — an infection of the <u>lungs</u> (see page 49).
>
> <u>Polio</u> — an infection of the intestine and <u>nervous system</u> that can cause <u>paralysis</u>.

4) It's not just humans that microorganisms infect though, <u>animals</u> can be infected too, e.g. <u>foot and mouth</u> affects some <u>hooved animals</u> such as cattle, sheep and pigs. It causes <u>fever</u>, <u>blisters</u> on <u>mouth</u> and <u>feet</u> and a <u>decline in milk yields</u>.

3) Fungi are Living Cells

You don't need to know much about fungi but they do cause two common diseases:

> <u>Athlete's foot</u> — a common fungal infection causing <u>painful itchy feet</u>.
>
> <u>Ringworm</u> — a fungal infection causing a <u>sore red ring</u> on the <u>skin</u> (it's not a worm).

Yawning is infectious — but not a disease thankfully...

There are about <u>10 times</u> more <u>bacterial cells</u> in your body than there are <u>human cells</u>... which is a pretty weird thought. Most of them are in your <u>digestive system</u> — they actually help your digestion. They're sometimes called 'good bacteria', while the nasty fellas on this page are labelled 'bad bacteria'.

The Spread of Infectious Disease

All these nasty little microorganisms can be spread from one person to another in various ways...

There are Seven Main Ways Infectious Diseases Can be Spread

The good thing is, if we know how infectious diseases are spread, we know how to reduce the spread.

1) DROPLETS IN THE AIR

Microorganisms get into the air when infected people cough and sneeze. If someone breathes them in they could get infected. Influenza (flu) and common cold viruses can be spread this way.

GRAPES / MICHAUD / SCIENCE PHOTO LIBRARY

Avoiding ill people — avoiding people with the sniffles will decrease your chances of catching airborne diseases. People with very contagious infections are sometimes isolated in hospital for the same reason.

2) DUST

Some microorganisms are pretty hardy and can stay alive in dust and dirt for a good while.

Making sure that food preparation surfaces and surgical instruments are cleaned thoroughly.

3) INSECTS

When insects feed on an infected animal they can take up microorganisms from their blood. When they feed on another animal the microorganism can be passed on. Malaria is spread this way by mosquitos.

Avoiding being bitten — by using insect nets, long clothing and insecticides.

4) FAECES

Microorganisms can pass out of the body in faeces. If the faeces then gets into food or water the microorganisms in it can easily infect other people. E.g. cholera can spread by faecal contamination of water.

Close monitoring of water systems and good sewage treatment. Practising good personal hygiene (see next page) can also help.

5) ANIMALS

Animals suffer from a range of diseases caused by microorganisms, some of which can infect humans. The movement of livestock around the country can spread diseases between farms.

Isolating infected animals and vaccinating livestock helps control the spread of disease.

6) BLOOD

Microorganisms can be spread by direct contact of bodily fluids such as blood, e.g. HIV (a virus) can be spread by sharing needles.

Avoiding direct contact with blood — don't share needles, syringes or razors.

7) TOUCH

Microorganisms can be spread by touching contaminated objects, e.g. snotty tissues.

Avoiding close contact with contaminated objects, and practising good personal hygiene.

If you're ill — please don't keep in touch...

Microbiologists are clever people — studying who gets ill and who doesn't helps scientists figure out how a disease is spread. And if they know how it's spread they can do something to stop it.

Preventing the Spread of Infectious Disease

To protect yourself against all those evil little microorganisms lurking around there are a few general things you can do (most of them involve being hygienic and clean — so go get your marigolds out).

There are Loads of Other Ways to Reduce the Spread of Disease

PRACTISING GOOD PERSONAL HYGIENE

1) Washing your hands — e.g. after you've been to the toilet, handled raw meat or been digging for worms. This reduces the chance of nasty pathogens that may have got on your hands being transferred to your mouth, eyes or nose (where they can get into the body and cause disease).

2) Protective clothing — covering up when in close contact with pathogens, e.g. wearing rubber gloves while cleaning the toilet (which I'm sure you do all the time), helps to stop pathogens getting from your hands into your body.

HEAT AND RADIATION — TO STERILISE

1) Using high temperatures — heat is used to kill microorganisms on surgical equipment so the patient doesn't get infected.

2) Using radiation — some things can't be sterilised using heat because they'd melt, e.g. plastic surgical equipment. Instead they're bombarded with radiation, this kills all the microorganisms on the equipment.

DISINFECTING SURFACES

1) Disinfectants are chemicals that kill microorganisms, e.g. bleach and chlorine.

2) They're used to kill microorganisms on surfaces, e.g. on lab benches, kitchen worktops and hospital ward floors. This means there are fewer pathogens that can be transferred from the surface to the body.

3) Disinfectants are normally pretty toxic so you can't use them to disinfect skin.

DISINFECTING SKIN USING ANTISEPTICS

1) Antiseptics are also chemicals that kill microorganisms. They include things like alcohol and iodine.

2) They're less toxic than disinfectants so they're used to kill microorganisms on skin.

3) Alcohol is often used to clean the skin before injections and iodine is used to clean cuts and to clean the skin before surgery (it makes the skin orange).

OTHER WAYS

1) Keeping kitchens hygienic — if kitchen surfaces are clean there are fewer pathogens that can get onto food that you eat.

2) Cooking food properly — this kills any pathogens that may be present in food so you're less likely to get food poisoning.

3) Avoiding unprotected sex — this reduces the chance of contracting sexually transmitted infections like HIV and herpes. Not having sex is the only sure-fire way of prevention.

There are more bacteria on the kitchen sink than the toilet seat...

For your exam you need to learn the ways to reduce the spread of disease, plus it'll come in pretty handy for your own day to day life too, unless you enjoy diarrhoea and vomiting that is.

The Body Fighting Off Disease

Even if you're the most hygienic person on the planet you'll still end up being exposed to microorganisms. But not to worry, your body has two main lines of defence against them: firstly it stops the little nasties from getting in, and secondly it destroys them if they do manage to get past the first line of defence.

Skin, Hairs and Mucus Stop Microorganisms Getting In

1) Hairs and mucus in your respiratory tract (breathing pipework) prevent a lot of nasties getting inside your body.

2) Your skin also acts as a huge barrier to microorganisms. If this gets broken, e.g. you cut yourself, small fragments of cells (called platelets, see p.51) help your blood clot, which seals up the gap. This prevents microorganisms getting into the body through cuts.

The Immune System Attacks Microorganisms that Do Get In

If something does make it through the first defences, your immune system kicks in. The most important part of your immune system is the white blood cells. These clever little cells travel around in your blood, looking for microorganisms. When they find some they have two main lines of attack:

Producing antibodies

1) Every invading pathogen has unique molecules (called antigens) on its surface.

2) When your white blood cells come across a foreign antigen (i.e. one they don't recognise), they'll start to produce chemicals called antibodies to lock on to and kill the invading pathogens. The antibodies produced are specific to that type of antigen — they won't lock on to any others.

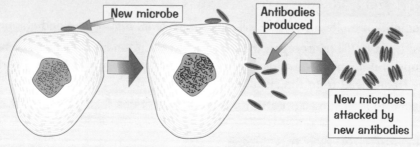

New microbe | Antibodies produced | New microbes attacked by new antibodies

3) Antibodies are then produced rapidly and flow all round the body to kill all similar bacteria or viruses.

4) If the person is infected with the same pathogen again, the white blood cells will rapidly produce the antibodies to kill it — the person is naturally immune to that pathogen and will be able to fight it off.

Engulfing them

White blood cells can engulf foreign cells and digest them.

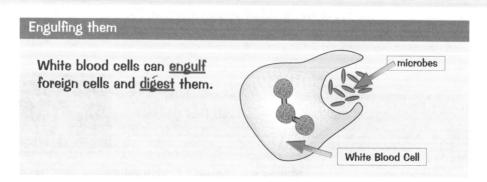

microbes

White Blood Cell

Fight disease — blow your nose with boxing gloves...

So by now you might have worked out that if you have a low level of white blood cells you'll be more susceptible to infections. In fact, HIV/AIDS doesn't kill people directly — it just makes it easier for something else to by attacking white blood cells and weakening the immune system. However, other diseases (e.g. leukaemia) can increase the number of white blood cells — and that's no good either.

Immunisation

The body's pretty good at fending off pathogens but some infections can be pretty serious. Scientists have developed a way to <u>protect</u> against some of these infections — <u>immunisation</u>. <u>Preventing</u> the disease from happening in the first place. Grand.

Immunisations <u>Help to</u> <u>Prevent</u> <u>Disease</u>

1) When you're infected with a <u>new</u> microorganism it can take your white blood cells a while to produce the antibodies to deal with it. In that time you can get <u>very ill</u>, or maybe even die.

2) To avoid this you can be <u>immunised</u> against some diseases, e.g. <u>measles</u>, <u>mumps</u> and <u>rubella</u> (using the MMR vaccine), <u>polio</u> and <u>tuberculosis</u> (TB).

> It's especially important that <u>girls</u> are <u>immunised</u> against <u>rubella</u> as it can be passed from a mother to an <u>unborn child</u>. This can cause serious <u>birth defects</u>, e.g. deafness.

3) Here's how immunisation works:

① Immunisation involves injecting <u>dead or weakened</u> microorganisms into the body.

Dead measles microbes

Antibodies produced

White blood cell

② These carry <u>antigens</u>, so even though they're <u>harmless</u> your body makes <u>antibodies</u> to attack them.

If measles microbes try to attack

No time off school...

They are recognised quickly and attacked

Antibodies

③ If <u>live</u> microorganisms of the <u>same type</u> appear after that, they'll be <u>killed immediately</u> because the body can produce the <u>right antibodies</u> much more <u>quickly</u> the second time around.

1) Immunisations have helped <u>control</u> lots of infectious diseases that were once <u>common</u> in the UK (e.g. polio, measles, whooping cough, rubella, mumps, TB, tetanus...).

2) And if an outbreak does occur, immunisations can <u>slow down</u> or <u>stop</u> the spread — if people don't catch the disease, they can't pass it on.

3) Immunisation is now used all over the world. <u>Smallpox</u> no longer occurs at all, and <u>polio</u> infections have fallen by 99%.

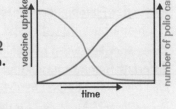

In the exam you might be asked to <u>interpret</u> a graph about vaccines and diseases. Don't panic — just take each line on the graph in turn and <u>explain what happens to it</u>, e.g. whether it goes up, or down or stays level.

Prevention is better than cure...

Immunisations are great — but they can have downsides too you know. Sometimes they don't give you <u>immunity</u> and you might even have a <u>bad reaction</u> to them. It's important to <u>balance the risks</u> — if you're not immunised you run the risk of catching the disease, but if you are, you might have a bad reaction. Most of the time you're much <u>safer with an immunisation</u> — you're more likely to have complications if you catch a disease than you are from having the vaccine.

Use of Drugs to Treat Disease

Immunisations and living hygienically can help prevent disease — but if you do get a disease you need to be able to treat it. Drugs are constantly being developed to treat diseases.

Drugs Can be Beneficial or Harmful

1) Drugs are substances that alter the way the body works. Some drugs are medically useful, such as antibiotics (e.g. penicillin). But many drugs can be dangerous if misused (see p.64 - p.65).

2) This is why you can buy some drugs over the counter at a pharmacy, but others are restricted — you can only get them on prescription, your doctor decides if you should have them.

Different Drugs Target Different Microorganisms

If your immune system can't fight off a disease then drugs can help.
There are different drugs for different types of microorganism.

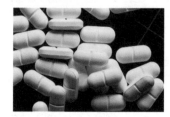

1) Antibiotics (e.g. penicillin) — fight against bacteria. They actually kill (or harm) the bacteria causing the problem without killing your own body cells. However, antibiotics don't destroy viruses as they're very different from bacteria.

2) Antivirals — fight against viruses. These are usually developed to treat very serious viral illnesses (such as AIDS and hepatitis). Flu and colds are caused by viruses. Usually you just have to wait for your body to deal with the virus, and relieve the symptoms if you start to feel really grotty.

Symptoms are physical signs of illness, e.g. coughing, sneezing or headaches.

3) Antifungals — fight against fungi. They can cure fungal infections such as athlete's foot and ringworm.

Antibiotics Are Produced By Microorganisms

1) Antibiotics are chemicals produced by bacteria and fungi that target specific bacteria.

2) Alexander Fleming discovered the first ever antibiotic called penicillin in 1928. It's made by a mould called *Penicillium* (a type of fungi).

3) Since the discovery of penicillin loads of other fungi and bacteria have been used to make different types of antibiotic. Scientists are trying to develop new antibiotics, which is just as well because bacteria evolve very quickly to become resistant to certain ones.

4) Bacteria and fungi can be genetically engineered to produce antibiotics in large quantities.

5) The discovery of antibiotics revolutionised medicine, allowing people with simple bacterial infections to be treated quickly and easily.

After Fleming there was no more phlegm-ing...

Alexander Fleming won the Nobel Prize thanks to antibiotics. All because he was a bit lazy, he booked himself a last minute holiday (two weeks in the Algarve, half board) and couldn't be bothered cleaning up his experiments. When he got home his experimental plates had gone mouldy, but he noticed that the bacteria had only grown in certain places. He discovered that this was because the bacteria had been killed by an antibiotic from a fungi that had drifted in from another lab. Pretty lucky really.

Use of Drugs to Treat Disease

Scientists can't just develop a new antibiotic and sell it to the general public straight away (as I once found out, the hard way) — it has to be <u>tested</u> first to make sure it works and that it's <u>safe</u>.

Antibiotics **are** Developed **and Then Thoroughly** Tested

This is what usually happens...

1 <u>Computer models</u> are often used in the early stages of drug development — these <u>simulate</u> a human's response to a drug. This can <u>identify promising drugs</u> to be tested in the next stage (but sometimes it's not as accurate as actually seeing the effect on a <u>live organism</u>).

2 Drugs are then developed further by testing on <u>human tissues</u> in the lab. However, you can't use human tissue to test drugs that affect <u>whole</u> or <u>multiple</u> body systems, e.g. testing the <u>side effects</u> of an antibiotic must be done on a whole animal with an intact circulatory system.

3 The next step is to develop and test the drug using <u>live animals</u>. The law in Britain states that any new drug must be tested on <u>two</u> different <u>live mammals</u>.

4 After the drug has been tested on animals it's tested on <u>healthy human volunteers</u> in a small <u>clinical trial</u> — this should determine whether there are any <u>side effects</u>. If the drug doesn't have too many side effects it's then tested on a <u>small</u> number of <u>patients</u>, and then a <u>large</u> number of patients. At each stage a '<u>control group</u>' is given an identical-looking tablet (called a <u>placebo</u>). This is done so scientists can see if the drug is having an effect and the patients don't just feel better because they <u>think</u> they're being treated.

There are Issues **Surrounding** Drug Testing

Here are a few arguments for and against testing drugs on animals:

1) Some people think that testing drugs on animals is <u>cruel</u>.

2) Others believe this is the <u>safest</u> way to make sure a drug <u>isn't dangerous</u> before it's given to humans.

3) Some people think that animals are <u>so different</u> from humans that testing on animals is <u>pointless</u>.

4) Other people think that mammals have <u>very similar</u> body systems and genes to humans (especially primates, e.g. monkeys) so they are a <u>good model</u> of how a drug might work in humans.

5) Some people believe that the suffering caused to animals <u>doesn't outweigh the benefits</u> of testing the drug on animals. Other people think that it <u>does</u>.

The UK animal testing regulations are some of the strictest in the world. When doing <u>research</u>, scientists are required to <u>replace</u> animal testing with another method if possible, <u>reduce</u> the number of animals used as much as they can and <u>refine</u> the experimental techniques used to minimise pain. However, to test <u>finished drugs</u> animals must be used — it's the <u>law</u>.

They did a lot of drugs testing in the sixties...

Testing drugs before they're used is <u>pretty important</u> — it'd be a bit rubbish if the drug didn't work or made you really ill. Whatever your view on <u>animal testing</u> make sure you know <u>both sides</u> of the story.

Recreational Drugs

Some drugs are also used _recreationally_ (i.e. just for fun). Some of these are _legal_, others _illegal_. They can _all_ cause harm to the body, but some are _more harmful_ than others.

Solvents _Affect the_ Lungs _and_ Neurones

Solvents are useful chemicals, but are misused as _drugs_ (by _inhaling_ the fumes).

1) Solvents are found in lighter fuel, spray paints, aerosols, thinners and dry cleaning fluids. (They can be _dangerous_ to people who _work_ with them, even if they don't deliberately _inhale_ them.)

2) Solvents act on the _nervous system_. They slow down messages as they're passed along _neurones_ (and can cause all sorts of damage as well).

3) Solvent abuse often causes _brain damage_ in the long term — this could show up as a personality change, sleeplessness or short-term memory loss.

4) Most solvents also irritate the _lungs_ and the _breathing passages_. Continued use risks the build-up of fluid in the lungs, causing _breathing difficulties_.

5) They can also cause _heart attacks_, which can cause _death_.

Some Misused Drugs _Also Have_ Medical Uses

Here are two examples of misused drugs and their use in medicine...

1) Opiates

1) _Opiates_ include _heroin_ and _morphine_ — they all come from the opium poppy.

2) Heroin is _highly addictive_ and _very dangerous_, especially when _mixed_ with _other substances_ like alcohol. An overdose can cause _heart failure_, _unconsciousness_, _coma_ or even _death_.

Medical Use
Opiates are _all painkillers_. Morphine's used by _doctors_ to treat severe pain — it's very _effective_. But just like heroin, morphine's very _addictive_, and so it's _illegal_ without a _prescription_.

2) Cannabis

1) _Cannabis_ can cause _panic_ and _paranoia_ as well as effects _associated with smoking tobacco_. (See next page for more.)

2) There's also some evidence that it can cause _mental health conditions_ such as _depression_ and _schizophrenia_.

Medical Use
Cannabis has been used as a _medicine_ for centuries, but it's now _illegal_. Recent research seems to suggest that cannabis can provide _benefit_ for _some_ patients — like _multiple sclerosis_ sufferers. Cannabis is still _illegal_ but some scientists are trying to identify the _beneficial chemicals_ in cannabis so they can make new drugs.

Learn all about drugs — and then forget them...

Some drugs can have major effects on your body, and the _more you take_ (and the _more often_ you take it) the _more likely_ you are to _damage_ your body. (That _doesn't_ mean you can take a little every once in a while and you won't get hurt though — some drugs, e.g. solvents, can _kill you_ the first time you take them.)

Recreational Drugs

You might think that just because <u>alcohol</u> and <u>tobacco</u> are <u>legal</u> they don't do you much <u>harm</u>. Well, think again. They <u>can</u> cause serious harm and you need to know all about them...

Drinking Alcohol Can Damage the Liver and Brain

1) The main effect of alcohol is to <u>reduce the activity</u> of the <u>nervous system</u> — slowing your reactions.

2) It can also make you feel <u>less inhibited</u> — which can help people to socialise and relax with each other.

3) However, too much leads to <u>impaired judgement</u>, <u>poor balance</u> and <u>coordination</u>, <u>lack of self-control</u>, <u>unconsciousness</u>, <u>coma</u> and even <u>death</u>.

4) Alcohol in excess causes <u>dehydration</u>. It can also damage <u>brain cells</u>, causing a noticeable <u>drop</u> in <u>brain function</u>. And too much drinking causes <u>severe damage</u> to the <u>liver</u>, leading to <u>liver disease</u>.

5) There are <u>social</u> costs too. Alcohol is linked with way more than half of <u>murders</u>, <u>stabbings</u> and <u>domestic assaults</u>. Alcohol misuse is also a factor in loads of <u>divorces</u> and cases of <u>child abuse</u>.

Smoking Tobacco Can Cause Quite a Few Problems Too

It affects the circulatory system...

1) Tobacco smoke contains <u>carbon monoxide</u> — this affects red blood cells and their ability to carry <u>oxygen</u>. In pregnant women, this can deprive the <u>foetus</u> of oxygen, making the baby <u>underweight</u>.

2) Smoking also causes <u>disease</u> of the <u>heart</u> and <u>blood vessels</u> — this can lead to <u>heart attacks</u> and <u>strokes</u>.

...and the respiratory system

1) Cigarette smoke damages the <u>lungs</u> (leading to diseases like <u>emphysema</u> and <u>bronchitis</u>).

2) <u>Tobacco smoke</u> contains <u>carcinogens</u> — chemicals that can lead to <u>cancer</u>. Lung cancer is <u>way more common</u> among <u>smokers</u> than non-smokers.

3) The <u>tar</u> in cigarettes damages the <u>cilia</u> (little hairs) in your lungs and windpipe. These hairs, along with <u>mucus</u>, catch a load of <u>dust</u> and <u>microbes</u> before they reach the lungs. When these cilia are damaged, it's harder for your body to eject stuff that shouldn't be there, which makes <u>chest infections</u> more likely.

And to top it all off, smoking tobacco is <u>addictive</u> — due to the <u>nicotine</u> in tobacco smoke.

Passive Smoking Can Be Also Very Harmful

A smoker inhales <u>only 15%</u> of the smoke from a cigarette — <u>the rest</u> goes into the <u>surrounding air</u> and <u>other people can breath it in</u>. When you breath in second hand smoke this is called <u>passive smoking</u>.

1) So, passive smokers can breath in the <u>same substances</u> as smokers — like <u>carbon monoxide</u> and <u>carcinogens</u>. And can suffer the same effects.

2) The risk of <u>lung cancer</u> is thought to rise significantly in non-smokers if they're <u>regularly exposed</u> to tobacco smoke.

Some countries have banned smoking in <u>public places</u>, like bars and restaurants — mainly because of the damage it can cause to other peoples' health.

The tar in cigarettes make cilia black...

So, just because the boys in blue won't come knocking on your door if you do it, <u>doesn't</u> necessarily mean it's a <u>good idea</u> — using giant fish heads as slippers isn't illegal but it's definitely not a good idea.

Genetic Disorders

Not all diseases are caused by microorganisms — a fair few are caused by an unhealthy lifestyle and some are caused by faulty genes.

Some Diseases have Genetic Causes

1) You inherit things like your eye colour, shape of nose, blood group etc. from your parents. But the problem is that genetic diseases can also be inherited.
2) This means you're born with a disease (though it might not cause a problem till later in life).
3) You immune system doesn't try to 'fight it off' because it's not caused by a microorganism.
4) A small number of genetic diseases can be cured (by bone marrow transplant).
5) Most genetic diseases can't be cured at the moment (though scientists are trying to change this).

Cystic Fibrosis is the Most Common Genetic Disease in the UK

It affects lots of people and currently can't be cured. It's due to one faulty gene...

1) This faulty gene causes a whole host of problems — like thick sticky mucus in the air passages and the digestive system.
2) People with this disease can suffer from things like chest infections and coughing.
3) There's no cure at the moment but the gene responsible has been identified and scientists are working to find a cure.
4) Treatment usually includes physiotherapy, medication and exercise.
5) Cystic fibrosis can be diagnosed by genetic testing, X-rays of the lungs and analysing the sweat of the suspected sufferer.
6) People only develop this disease if they have inherited the faulty gene from both parents.

Huntington's Chorea Affects the Nervous System

This genetic disease is also caused by a single faulty gene and no cure has yet been found.

1) The faulty gene affects the production of certain chemicals in the brain. This causes damage to nerve cells in the brain.
2) This damage can result in gradual loss of function of areas of the brain that effect movement, understanding and behaviour.
3) It results in shaking, erratic body movements and eventually severe mental deterioration.
4) The onset of these symptoms can be anywhere between 20 and 50 years old.
5) Treatment includes medication, developing communication and a high calorie diet.
6) Genetic testing can help diagnose sufferers.
7) People will develop this disease if they inherit just one faulty gene, from either parent.

We know of over 4000 different genetic diseases...

Scientists are still quite iffy about which genes cause many genetic diseases. But then with so many, who can blame them really. There are loads of scientists working on this at the moment, busily trying to work out how to cure genetic diseases and find genes linked to other diseases.

Revision Summary 2 for Section 2.2

Well, after all that I think I'm turning into a hypochondriac, with an obsessive compulsive disorder for cleaning, and I don't think I'll ever touch another drop of alcohol again. Ha, who am I kidding, this revision summary is enough to turn even a nun into a cigarette wielding alcoholic. Enjoy.

1) What is the name given to microorganisms that cause disease?
2) Give two ways bacteria can make you feel ill.
3) Give two illnesses *Staphylococcus aureus* can cause?
4) Name three diseases caused by viruses.
5) Name two common diseases caused by fungi?
6) How can microorganisms get into droplets in the air?
7) Give three ways you can reduce the spread of microorganisms carried by insects.
8) How can you reduce the spread of disease by livestock?
9) Why should you wash your hands regularly?
10) Give two ways surgical equipment can be sterilised.
11) What type of chemicals can be used to kill microorganisms on your skin?
12) How does cooking your food properly reduce your risk of getting ill?
13) How does your body prevent microorganisms from getting in?
14) What do white blood cells produce to kill invading pathogens?
15) How does exposure to dead or weakened microorganisms help to fight future infections of the same type?
16) Why is it especially important for girls to be immunised against rubella?
17) Give an example of a disease which has been completely wiped out thanks to immunisations.
18) What are drugs?
19) What type of microorganism do antibiotics kill?
20) Give an example of an illness that antivirals treat.
21) Who discovered the first antibiotic?
22) Outline the four main stages of antibiotic testing.
23) Why do clinical trials need to be carried out on humans?
24) Give two arguments in favour and two arguments against drugs testing on animals.
25) Name two long term effects of solvent abuse.
26) Where do opiates come from?
27) Name an opiate which is used in medicine. What is it used for?
28) Name a mental health condition that might be linked to the use of cannabis.
29) What physical health condition is cannabis thought to benefit?
30) Name two organs that can be severely affected by alcohol abuse.
31) Name three harmful substances in tobacco smoke.
32) Suggest why some countries have banned smoking in public places.
33) What causes the symptoms of cystic fibrosis?
34) Huntington's disease is a genetic disease, what effect does the faulty gene have?
35) Give two symptoms of Huntington's disease.

Classifying Chemicals

Most of the substances we use can be found in the Earth. Useful elements (like sulfur and gold) can occur naturally on their own, as can useful compounds (like limestone). But some useful substances are in mixtures or compounds with other things, e.g. salt in rock salt and metals in metal ores. So before you even get started on those things, you've got to be clear on what elements, compounds and mixtures are...

Elements are Made Up of Just One Type of Atom

1) As you probably know, all substances are made up of atoms.

2) If a substance only contains only one type of atom it's called an element.
   Quite a lot of everyday substances are elements:

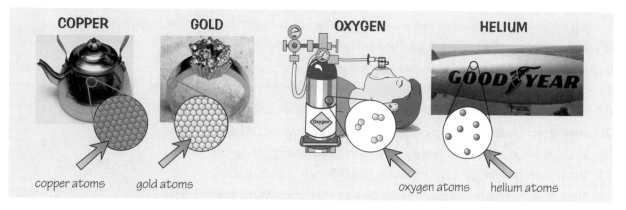

COPPER   GOLD   OXYGEN   HELIUM

copper atoms   gold atoms   oxygen atoms   helium atoms

Compounds and Mixtures Contain Different Types of Atom

1) If there's more than one type of atom, e.g. copper and oxygen, it's either a mixture or a compound.

2) A compound is where different atoms have bonded together chemically, e.g. salt, limestone.

3) A mixture contains different substances that are not chemically bonded together, e.g. rock salt.

4) Mixtures are generally easier to separate than compounds. (See p.74 for more on separating.)

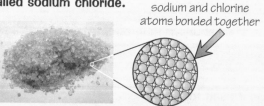

SALT is a COMPOUND of sodium and chlorine, called sodium chloride.

sodium and chlorine atoms bonded together

LIMESTONE is a COMPOUND of calcium, carbon and oxygen, called calcium carbonate.

calcium, carbon and oxygen atoms bonded together

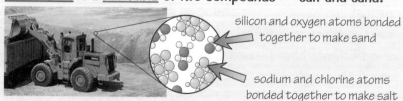

ROCK SALT is a MIXTURE of two compounds — salt and sand.

silicon and oxygen atoms bonded together to make sand

sodium and chlorine atoms bonded together to make salt

So next time you're at St Paul's Cathedral eating salty chips...

...you can thank the Earth for making it all possible (or not — up to you). Cover the rest of the page and fill in this table with the substances below:
salt, rock salt, oxygen, crude oil, limestone, gold

Elements	Compounds	Mixtures

Chemical Symbols and Notation

Writing out the names of chemicals all the time can be a bit of a drag. That's why scientists invented chemical symbols — these let you write down any element using only one or two letters. Beautiful.

Atoms Can be Represented by Symbols

Atoms of each element can be represented by a one or two letter symbol — it's a type of shorthand that saves you the bother of having to write the full name of the element.

Some make perfect sense, for example:

C = carbon   O = oxygen   Mg = magnesium

Others seem to make about as much sense as an apple with a handle. For example:

Na = sodium   Fe = iron   Pb = lead

Most of these odd symbols actually come from the Latin names of the elements.

Some Elements are Metals and Some are Non-metals

There are about a hundred elements that chemists know about, but luckily you're not expected to know the chemical symbols for all of them. The ones you're expected to know are listed below — you have to be able to give the element's chemical symbol if you're told its name (and vice versa). Plus, you should know whether each one is a metal or a non-metal — there are ten of each.

Metals

1)	Aluminium	Al
2)	Barium	Ba
3)	Calcium	Ca
4)	Iron	Fe
5)	Lead	Pb
6)	Magnesium	Mg
7)	Potassium	K
8)	Silver	Ag
9)	Sodium	Na
10)	Zinc	Zn

Non-metals

1)	Bromine	Br
2)	Carbon	C
3)	Chlorine	Cl
4)	Fluorine	F
5)	Hydrogen	H
6)	Nitrogen	N
7)	Oxygen	O
8)	Phosphorus	P
9)	Silicon	Si
10)	Sulfur	S

All these exciting sciency symbols — I'm in my element...

Okay fine, I admit it. This is dull. It's got to be learnt though, so the best thing to do is to close the book and try to write the symbol for each element in the list from memory. Then do it again. And don't worry — these little guys crop up so often in Chemistry that soon they'll all seem like old friends...

Chemical Building Blocks

In order to really <u>understand</u> different materials and so come up with the best ways to <u>use</u> them, chemists have to understand the <u>building blocks</u> from which all materials are made. A material's <u>properties</u> depend on the types of <u>atoms</u> it contains, and the way those atoms are <u>joined together</u>.

Atoms Have a Small Nucleus Surrounded by Electrons

Pick an object... <u>any</u> object. Whatever you've chosen, it's made up of small particles called <u>atoms</u> — all <u>matter</u> (stuff) is. And if you could look closely enough, you'd see that all the atoms look a bit like the one shown below — with even tinier particles called <u>protons</u>, <u>neutrons</u> and <u>electrons</u> arranged in a particular way.

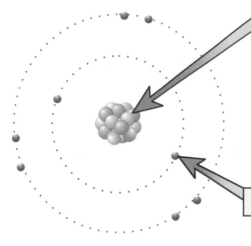

The Nucleus

1) The nucleus is in the <u>middle</u> of the atom.

2) It contains <u>protons</u> (⬤) and <u>neutrons</u> (⬤).

3) Almost the <u>whole mass</u> of the atom is <u>concentrated</u> in the <u>nucleus</u>.

4) But size-wise it's <u>tiny</u> compared to the atom as a whole.

The Electrons

1) Electrons move <u>around</u> the nucleus in <u>shells</u>.

2) They're <u>tiny</u>, but their paths cover a <u>lot of space</u>.

3) Electron shells explain the <u>whole of Chemistry</u>.

You can't see individual atoms with a magnifying glass — they're <u>way</u> too small. You could fit about 10 million atoms across the full stop at the end of this sentence.

Different Elements have Different Numbers of Protons

All atoms look pretty much like the picture above. The only thing that makes one chemical element different to all the rest is the <u>number</u> of protons, neutrons and electrons in its atoms.

1) It's the number of <u>protons</u> in the nucleus that decides what <u>type</u> of atom it is.

2) For example, an atom with <u>1 proton</u> in its nucleus is <u>hydrogen</u>, an atom with <u>2 protons</u> is <u>helium</u>, an atom with <u>8 protons</u> is <u>oxygen</u>, an atom with <u>79 protons</u> is <u>gold</u>... and so on and so on.

3) The number of protons in an atom is called the <u>atomic number</u>.

The number of <u>protons</u> in an atom is always the <u>same</u> as the number of <u>electrons</u>.

These bottles contain only <u>oxygen</u> atoms. So <u>all</u> the atoms contain <u>8 protons</u> and <u>8 electrons</u>.

These are bars of <u>pure gold</u> — they contain only atoms of <u>gold</u>. <u>All</u> the atoms contain <u>79 protons</u> and <u>79 electrons</u>.

The oxygen in the bottle and the gold bar are both <u>elements</u> — see page 68.

Basic atom facts — they don't take up much space...

Two main points on this page...

1) If you look <u>really</u> closely, all atoms look roughly the same — with a cluster of protons and neutrons in the middle and electrons whizzing round the outside.

2) If you know the <u>number of protons</u> (or electrons), you know <u>what kind</u> of atom it is, and vice versa.

Compounds and Formulas

So, you know that <u>elements</u> are made up of just <u>one type</u> of atom, all with the <u>same</u> number of protons and electrons. You also know the <u>symbols</u> for some of those elements. Now the fun begins as you start sticking elements together to make <u>compounds</u>, and sticking their symbols together to make <u>formulas</u>.

A Formula Shows What Atoms are in a Compound

<u>Compounds</u>, remember, are substances that contain <u>more than one kind</u> of atom bonded together.

1) <u>Carbon dioxide</u> is a <u>compound</u> — it contains carbon atoms and oxygen atoms.

2) In fact, every molecule of carbon dioxide contains <u>1 carbon atom</u> and <u>2 oxygen atoms</u>.

There you go... a molecule of carbon dioxide — one carbon atom and two oxygen atoms.

3) Using <u>chemical symbols</u>, this would be: CO_2 Easy.

An atom of carbon... ...and two atoms of oxygen.

You Need to Know the Formulas of Some Compounds

There are <u>twenty</u> that you need to learn. You have to know the <u>name</u> of the compound if you're given its <u>formula</u>, and likewise if you're given the name you have to be able to write the formula.

1)	Ammonia	NH_3		11)	Barium chloride	$BaCl_2$
2)	Carbon dioxide	CO_2		12)	Sodium chloride	$NaCl$
3)	Methane	CH_4		13)	Calcium carbonate	$CaCO_3$
4)	Water	H_2O		14)	Copper carbonate	$CuCO_3$
5)	Hydrochloric acid	HCl		15)	Sodium carbonate	Na_2CO_3
6)	Sulfuric acid	H_2SO_4		16)	Potassium nitrate	KNO_3
7)	Calcium oxide	CaO		17)	Silver nitrate	$AgNO_3$
8)	Iron oxide	Fe_2O_3		18)	Barium sulfate	$BaSO_4$
9)	Lead oxide	PbO		19)	Copper sulfate	$CuSO_4$
10)	Sodium hydroxide	$NaOH$		20)	Sodium sulfate	Na_2SO_4

Chemical Equations Show the Atoms Involved in Reactions

1) A <u>chemical reaction</u> is when atoms are 'shuffled around'.

2) For example, when you <u>burn</u> a lump of <u>carbon</u>, a chemical reaction takes place. The carbon combines with <u>oxygen</u> from the air to form <u>carbon dioxide</u>:

An atom of carbon combines with two atoms of oxygen...

...and forms a molecule of carbon dioxide.

3) A <u>chemical equation</u> just shows the same information about a reaction — '<u>what goes in</u>' and '<u>what comes out</u>'.

$$C + O_2 \rightarrow CO_2$$

4) The things on the <u>left hand side</u> of the equation are <u>reactants</u>. These react to form things on the <u>right side</u> of the equation — the <u>products</u>.

H_2O, CO_2, DVD, FBI, GSOH...

Do the same here as you did for the elements — make a list of the <u>20 compounds</u>, then shut the book and try to write the <u>formula</u> for each one next to the name. Then try it the other way round.

Organic and Inorganic Chemicals

Now you know all about compounds it's about time we got down to the gritty subject of classifying them. There are two broad categories that scientists use: inorganic and organic (not to be confused with food).

Chemicals Can be Organic...

There are literally millions of chemicals (that we know of). To make their lives easier, scientists organise these chemicals into groups. One of the simplest ways to organise chemicals is based on whether or not they contain carbon.

1) Most chemicals that contain carbon are called organic chemicals. The original meaning of the word organic is 'derived from living matter'. All living organisms contain carbon — and organic chemicals usually come from living things.

2) These chemicals are definitely organic. They all contain carbon (check the formulas). They also all come from living things — even coal and crude oil (see below and p.75).

Chemical	Formula	Use	Source
Ethanol	C_2H_5OH	Drinks	Plants
Ethene	C_2H_4	Plastics	Crude oil
Phenol	C_6H_5OH	Making drugs	Coal

...Or Inorganic

It's not quite as simple as this though. Some compounds that contain carbon (e.g. carbonates) are inorganic.

1) Most inorganic chemicals don't contain carbon. They usually come from things that have never lived.

Chemical	Formula	Use	Source
Iron	Fe	Building material	Iron ore
Aluminium silicate	Al_2SiO_5	Used in bricks	Clay
Potassium sulfate	K_2SO_4	Fertiliser	Rocks

If you look at the source of the chemicals, you can see that they come from non-living things.

2) The chemicals in the table contain no carbon — they're all inorganic. It's possible to tell if a chemical is organic or inorganic by looking at its formula.

Potassium sulfate: K_2SO_4
2 potassium, 1 sulfur, 4 oxygen. But no carbon — inorganic

Methane: CH_4
1 carbon, 4 hydrogen — organic

So, if a chemical's formula contains no carbon it's inorganic and probably comes from non-living material. If it's got carbon in its formula it's probably organic and it probably used to be alive.

Organic Substances are Pretty Useful

The majority of the chemicals we know about are organic. They're really important in day to day life.

1) Fossil fuels are organic chemicals — they form over millions of years from the buried remains of plants and animals.

2) Fossil fuels, like crude oil, contain a lot of carbon. This makes them a great source of organic substances, e.g. plastics, petrol and some medicines are all made from crude oil.

3) In fact, the vast majority of organic chemicals are derived from crude oil, even materials like nylon and polyester.

4) The products made from organic chemicals are really important in our lives — it's hard to imagine life without them. No TVs, computers or plastic drink bottles, and a lot less medicine to keep us healthy.

Organic chemicals — useful and tuneful...

You might find it hard to believe that plastics are derived from living matter. It doesn't mean they were actually alive — there weren't large lumps of plastic roaming the prehistoric plains like dinosaurs. Derived just means the chemicals they're made from came from once-living matter like plants and animals.

Useful Chemicals From Rocks

Many substances can be taken out of the ground by mining or quarrying. Some of these materials can be used <u>as they are</u>, but many are just the <u>starting material</u> to make other useful substances — by <u>separating</u> them into their constituent parts (see page 75) or by <u>combining</u> them with other materials.

Sulfur and Gold Can be Found in the Ground Ready to Use...

1) <u>Sulfur</u> is the <u>yellow</u>, powdery stuff you find in the ground near <u>volcanoes</u> and in <u>geothermal areas</u> that gives off a nasty <u>rotten-egg-smelling gas</u>. It's a <u>non-metal element</u> (see p.69).

2) Sulfur's <u>not very reactive</u>, so it tends to occur naturally <u>on its own</u> in the Earth, rather than with other substances.

3) Sulfur has many uses, including <u>fertilisers</u>, making <u>sulfuric acid</u> for <u>petrol refining</u> and <u>car batteries</u>, making <u>gunpowder</u> for guns (no really) and for <u>fireworks</u>.

A smoking, sulfur-rimmed crater in New Zealand. It smells.

1) <u>Gold</u> is a <u>metal element</u>. Like sulfur, gold is very <u>unreactive</u>, so it's usually found <u>on its own</u> in the ground, not bonded to other stuff.

2) It can be exposed by processes like river erosion, so you can sometimes find it in river beds. People used to '<u>pan</u>' for gold — they just <u>sifted</u> through the <u>mud and silt</u> from river beds, and picked out the <u>shiny grains</u>. Then they melted it all down to make nice tiaras and things.

3) The main <u>uses</u> of gold are for <u>jewellery</u> (clearly), and in situations where you want a metal that <u>won't react</u> with anything, such as in <u>tooth fillings</u> and in <u>electric circuits</u>.

...And So Can Limestone and Marble

<u>Limestone</u> and <u>marble</u> are both natural forms of <u>calcium carbonate</u> — a compound that can be <u>mined</u> straight from the ground.

LIMESTONE

<u>Limestone</u> is a rough, pale grey rock that's <u>easy to shape</u> into blocks for <u>building</u> with. It's also used to make <u>cement</u>, <u>glass</u> and <u>lime</u> (to put on acidic soil). For more uses of limestone, see page 84.

Some Uses of Limestone

MARBLE

<u>Marble</u> is a <u>bright white</u>, crystalline rock, often with veins of other minerals. It can be <u>polished</u> to a <u>shiny</u>, smooth finish, and can make impressive <u>statues</u>, <u>sculptures</u>, <u>palaces</u>, etc.

Some Uses of Marble

I feel like a stroll round a volcano — get out in the elements...

Some substances are useful in the form you find them. You just dig them out, give 'em a bit of a spit and polish, and Bob's your uncle you've got your very own Michelangelo's David. Well, almost.

Useful Chemicals From Rocks

Unfortunately not everything we dig up from the ground puts up as little <u>resistance</u> as <u>gold</u> and <u>marble</u>. Oh no, the likes of <u>salt</u> and <u>oil</u> (see next page) take a little more coaxing...

Most Salt Comes From Rock Salt Mines

1) The most obvious source of salt on Earth is the <u>oceans</u>, and in lots of (hot) countries they do get salt that way — they pump seawater into big open tanks and leave the Sun to <u>evaporate</u> off the water, leaving salt. But in fact, <u>less than a third</u> of the salt used by humans comes from seawater.

2) The majority comes from <u>rock salt mines</u> hundreds of metres below the surface of the Earth. These were left behind when <u>ancient seas</u> dried up. In Britain there are massive deposits of rock salt sitting innocently underneath <u>Cheshire</u>.

3) <u>Rock salt</u> is basically a <u>mixture</u> of <u>salt</u> (<u>sodium chloride</u>) and <u>sand</u>. It's either mined as rock salt, or just the salt can be obtained as <u>brine</u> (salt water) by pumping hot water underground to dissolve the salt. The salt solution is then pumped back to the surface.

4) In colder countries (like Britain) rock salt is used in its <u>unpurified</u> form to <u>de-ice</u> roads in winter. The salt melts the ice and the <u>sand</u> helps vehicles to grip the wet, slippery road.

Rock Salt Has to be Purified Before You Add it to Food

1) You've probably done that <u>experiment</u> in the lab where you get <u>pure salt</u> from rock salt...

- You <u>grind</u> up the rock salt, put it into a container and add <u>water</u>.
- Then you <u>heat</u> the water, gently <u>stirring</u> all the time, until all the salt has <u>dissolved</u>.
- You <u>filter</u> the mixture to remove the sand, and then leave the salt water until all the water has <u>evaporated</u> to give <u>salt crystals</u>.

2) When rock salt is purified <u>industrially</u> things get a bit more complicated, but the basic idea's the same.

- Chunks of rock salt are <u>crushed</u> in a machine and dissolved in water to form <u>brine</u>.
- The brine is filtered and treated with <u>chemicals</u> that remove most of the <u>impurities</u> left in the solution.
- Multiple stages of evaporation in a <u>vacuum evaporator</u> are then used to produce pure sodium chloride crystals, which are <u>dried</u> in a kiln.

Sodium Chloride is Used in Food and in the Chemical Industry

1) Salt is used in foods as a <u>preservative</u> and to add <u>flavour</u>.

2) Salt is also an important starting material for the <u>chemical industry</u> — <u>hydrogen</u>, <u>chlorine</u> and <u>sodium hydroxide</u> can be produced from salt solution. Molten salt can be used to produce sodium.

3) These products are used in all sorts of industries — making <u>plastics</u> and <u>pharmaceuticals</u> (chlorine), <u>ammonia</u> and <u>margarine</u> (hydrogen), <u>detergents</u> (sodium) and <u>ceramics</u>, <u>soap</u> and <u>paper</u> (sodium hydroxide) to name but a few.

Thanks for all your hard work — here's a bag of salt...

Back in the olden days when they didn't have fridges, salt was used to <u>preserve food</u>. People also used to be <u>paid</u> in salt — the word salary comes from the Latin word for salt, <u>sal</u>. Well... fancy that.

Useful Chemicals From Rocks

Salt isn't the only amazingly useful substance to be found just lying around in the Earth — crude oil is, if anything, even more useful. But to get the best out of it you have to separate out all its different parts — which is done using the fancy-sounding process of fractional distillation.

Fractional Distillation is Used to Separate Different Substances

1) Crude oil is extracted from the ground by drilling. Underground oil fields are found in many places, e.g. in the Middle East, and under the North Sea.

2) Crude oil is formed from the buried remains of plants and animals — so it's a fossil fuel (see p.92). Over millions of years, with high temperatures and pressures, the remains turn into crude oil.

3) Crude oil is a mixture of different chemicals called hydrocarbons. It's refined to separate it into different groups of chemicals called fractions, which contain molecules of a similar size. These have various different uses. The five that you need to know about are shown on the diagram below.

4) Crude oil is split into these different fractions using fractional distillation, as shown below:

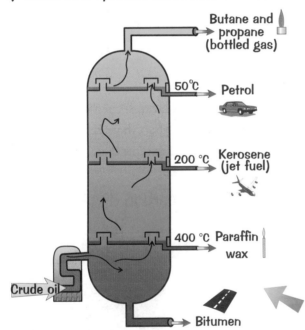

1) The crude oil is heated and the different chemicals evaporate and rise up the column.

2) The fractionating column becomes cooler the further up you go.

3) The different chemicals condense at different temperatures, so those with the lowest boiling points are collected near the top, and those with the highest are collected at the bottom.

4) The process works continuously, with heated crude oil piped in at the bottom and the various fractions being constantly collected.

You need to know that butane and propene (used as bottled gas fuels), petrol (used as car fuel), kerosene (used as aircraft fuel), paraffin wax (used as a lubricant and for candles) and bitumen (used for road surfaces and roofing) are all made from crude oil.

Crude Oil Fractions are Used as Fuels and as Raw Materials

1) Crude oil provides fuel for most modern transport and for heating, cooking, etc.

2) It also provides the raw materials for making various chemicals — for example: plastics, packaging, textiles, dyes, paints and lots of medicines.

3) Crude oil is a non-renewable resource, which means that one day it'll run out. Some scientists think that this will happen within the next fifty years.

4) Because it can be used as a fuel and to make drugs and we're running out of it, there's a bit of a conflict over how best we should use the remaining supplies of oil.

5) Some people argue that we should stop using it as a fuel immediately (because there are alternatives — see p.93-95) and just use it to make essential things like medicines.

6) But there's still a huge demand for crude oil as a fuel, because it's a convenient and concentrated energy source.

Quick everyone — buy solar-powered cars and nuclear ovens...

Some people get really passionate about how oil should be used, including examiners. In your exam, you could be asked to interpret data about the competing demands for of oil resources. You've been warned.

Extracting Metals From Rocks

It's not often you find big lumps of metal in the ground — more <u>reactive</u> metals like iron and lead tend to occur naturally as <u>compounds</u> (see p.68). The metal has to be extracted by <u>chemical methods</u>.

Ores Contain Enough Metal to Make Extraction Worthwhile

1) A <u>metal ore</u> is a mixture of a <u>mineral</u> and <u>surrounding rock</u>.

2) In many cases the ore is an <u>oxide</u> of the metal — it's bonded to oxygen. But not all ores are oxides. Here are a few examples:

> • One type of <u>iron ore</u> is called <u>haematite</u>. This is iron(III) oxide (Fe_2O_3).
> • The main <u>aluminium ore</u> is called <u>bauxite</u>. This is aluminium oxide (Al_2O_3).
> • Another type of <u>iron ore</u> is <u>pyrite</u>. This is iron disulfide (FeS_2).

Pyrite — also known as fool's gold.

3) Ores are "finite resources" — there's a <u>limited amount</u> of them. Once you've dug them all up there's no more.

Some Metals can be Extracted by Reduction with Carbon

Some metals can be <u>extracted</u> by <u>heating</u> the ore with <u>carbon</u> (usually in the form of coke — a type of coal) or <u>carbon monoxide</u> (made by burning coke). The fancy name for this is <u>reduction</u> — which simply means that the <u>oxygen</u> is <u>removed</u> — this makes it a 'pure' metal.

1) <u>Carbon</u> and <u>carbon monoxide</u> are <u>reducing agents</u> (they 'steal' the oxygen away from the metal).

2) This extraction method only works for metals that are <u>less reactive</u> than <u>carbon</u> though.

3) A good example is the reduction of <u>iron(III) oxide</u> (haematite) to <u>iron</u>. The end products of the reaction are <u>iron</u> and <u>carbon dioxide</u>. You need to be able to write the <u>word equation</u> for this reaction:

> iron(III) oxide   +   carbon monoxide $\rightarrow$ iron   +   carbon dioxide

Metal Extraction Can Have an Effect on the Environment

1) Mining metal ores can be <u>good</u> — many <u>useful products</u> can be made. It also provides local people with <u>jobs</u> and brings <u>money</u> into the area. This means services such as <u>transport</u> and <u>health</u> can be improved.

2) <u>But</u> mining ores is <u>bad for the environment</u> — it causes noise, dust, scarring of the landscape and loss of habitats. Local waterways may also be <u>polluted</u> by toxic heavy metals.

3) Mines produce a lot of <u>waste rock</u>, which has to be hauled away from the mine to waste dumps. This is a <u>waste of land</u>, and the increased <u>traffic</u> around the mine causes further <u>pollution</u>.

4) Today, scientists tend to be just as concerned with trying to <u>limit</u> the <u>negative effects</u> of metal extraction as with trying to find the most efficient ways to actually do it. Know these examples:

> a) <u>GAS SCRUBBING</u> — waste gas from extracting the metal from its ore is passed through water before being released — this <u>removes dust particles</u> from the gas. The water also contains chemicals that <u>remove toxic substances</u>.
>
> b) <u>USING WASTE GAS</u> — e.g. carbon monoxide can be used as a <u>heating fuel</u>. When it's burnt with oxygen, heat and carbon dioxide (which is safer than carbon monoxide) are produced.
>
> c) <u>TREATING CONTAMINATED WATER</u> — scientists are developing various ways to treat water contaminated with metals, e.g. using materials such as carbon filters to trap the contaminants.

Didn't know ironing was so complicated — I'll do the dishes...

Extracting metals using reduction with carbon sounds quite <u>clever</u> and <u>modern</u>, but actually people have been doing it since <u>1200 BC</u>. They probably didn't know the <u>equation</u> though, so they weren't that good.

Industrial Production of Chemicals

We use loads of chemicals like fertilisers every year — and they don't just fall off the back of a wagon (unless you're following a horse box). No, they have to be made — many everyday chemicals that we take for granted need to be manufactured on a massive scale.

Some Chemicals are Produced on a Large Scale...

There are certain chemicals that we just can't live without, and we produce thousands and thousands of tonnes of these every year. Chemicals that are produced on a large scale are called bulk chemicals — ammonia, poly(ethene) and sulfuric acid are three examples.

1) In Britain we use around a million tonnes of fertiliser every year. Fertiliser contains a lot of ammonia (among other things) so the chemical industry needs to make a fair bit of ammonia to meet the demand.

2) There's also poly(ethene) which is used to make loads of things like shopping bags, buckets and pipes. Because of all its uses we need to produce it on a massive scale.

3) You may have come across sulfuric acid in the lab at school. You might not think it, but sulfuric acid also has to be produced on a very large scale. A laboratory chemical is just one use of its uses — it's also used in car batteries and in the manufacture of steel and fertilisers.

...And Some are Produced on a Smaller Scale

Some chemicals aren't needed in such large amounts — but that doesn't mean they're any less important.

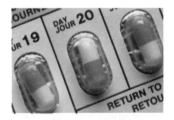

1) Chemicals produced on a smaller scale are called fine chemicals. Examples of these include medicines, dyes and pigments.

2) Unlike bulk chemicals, most fine chemicals require several different stages in their production.

3) Production is much more specialised and on a much smaller scale.

There are Lots of Different Jobs in the Chemical Industry

There are hundreds of different job opportunities in the chemical industry, because of the wide range of different chemicals that are produced. Some examples of jobs include:

1) Research and development — somebody has to come up with ideas for new products. Research scientists figure out what to make and how to make it, and they also make sure the product is safe. Some also work on making existing products better.

2) Designing or refining the manufacturing process — making several tonnes of a chemical on an industrial scale is quite different to making a small sample in a lab. Scientists are employed to make sure that large scale processes are safe, efficient and actually make money.

3) Quality control — most companies employ scientists to ensure that the quality of the product is consistent and up to scratch.

4) Environmental science — many industrial processes and products could potentially damage the environment. A lot of companies employ scientists to minimise this risk.

Fine chemicals — by appointment to Her Majesty, The Queen...

Aren't poly(ethene) bags just great — they're free, dead strong and don't do any harm at all to the environment. Oh no wait, I was thinking about trees. Poly(ethene) bags actually pose a significant threat to the environment — they've even been banned in Bangladesh. Kids — say no to plastic bags.

Industrial Production of Chemicals

Like everything in life, industrial chemical production is all about compromise
— good job my ex-wife isn't running the show.

Reactions Can be Speeded Up

In industry, time is money — so scientists have come up with ways of making chemical reactions faster.
There are a few ways to do this:

> 1) Raise the temperature.
>
> 2) Increase the concentration of the reactants
>   (if they're gases, increasing the pressure has the same effect).
>
> 3) Increase the surface area of the reactants (e.g. by breaking them into smaller chunks).
>
> 4) Add a catalyst (a chemical that speeds up a reaction but doesn't take part in the reaction).

1) This graph shows a reaction under normal conditions. The steepness of
   the graph tells you how fast the reaction is going — the steeper it is the
   faster it's going. When the graph becomes flat the reaction is complete.

2) This graph shows the reaction when one of the conditions
   is altered (e.g. a higher temperature or catalyst is used).
   The reaction goes faster (the slope is steeper) but the
   total amount of product produced stays the same.

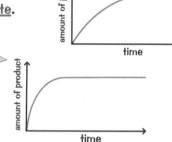

3) Controlling the rate of chemical reactions is really important
   in industry. For example if we ran some reactions at low temperature
   and with no catalyst they'd be far too slow to make any money.

4) But the temperature can't be raised too much — the costs would be too high, it would use lots of
   energy (which would probably come from burning fossil fuels) and it might be unsafe.

5) So a compromise must be reached between reaction speed and other factors like safety,
   environmental issues and costs.

Choosing the Right Process is Never Straightforward

You might be asked to interpret data about different manufacturing processes in the exam.
There are loads of different factors which must be taken into account when choosing which one is best
— running costs, the effect on the environment, etc.

EXAMPLE: **Three different processes (A, B and C) can be used to make a product. Which one is best?**

Process	Raw materials cost (£m)	Running costs (£m)	Waste produced	Product (tonnes)
A	20	11	Carbon dioxide, sulfur dioxide	550
B	32	15	Carbon monoxide	600
C	27	16	Steam	480

1) Process A has the lowest running and raw
   materials costs. But it does produce sulfur
   dioxide (which can cause acid rain) so you'd
   have to spend money making sure it didn't
   get into the atmosphere.

2) Process B produces the most product but has the highest costs. It also produces carbon
   monoxide (but this could be used as a heating fuel reducing costs elsewhere in the plant).

3) Process C is nearly as expensive as process B and has the lowest product yield but the
   waste produced doesn't damage the environment.

Whichever process you pick, remember to give reasons for your choice.

Celebrity pets — they're on the cat A-list...

Increasing the temperature and adding a catalyst only speed up a reaction. You still get the same
amount of product — just at a faster rate. The only way to get any more product is to use more
reactants. Also remember that if the reactants are gases, increasing the pressure also increases the rate.

Revision Summary for Section 2.3

Wow, what a truly great section that was. I can't remember the last time I had so much fun. I'm kind of sad that it's got to come to an end, but thankfully that doesn't have to happen just yet. First there are these exciting revision summary questions as a little memento of the good times we've enjoyed together. Then, I'm afraid you'll have to shed a little tear and move on with your life. Oh, how I love mining.

1)* How many different types of atoms does the element silicon contain?

2) What is meant by the terms compound and mixture? Give an example of each.

3) Which are easier to separate — mixtures or compounds?

4) Give the chemical symbol for the element sodium.

5) Which element is represented by the chemical symbol P?

6) Which of the following symbols does <u>not</u> represent a metal element: F, Pb, Ag?

7) Which particles are found grouped in the centre of an atom?

8)* An atom of fluorine has nine protons. How many electrons does it have?

9)* An atom has fourteen protons. Use a periodic table to find out which element it is.

10)* The formula for sulfuric acid is H_2SO_4. How many atoms are there altogether in one molecule of sulfuric acid?

11) Give the formula for the compound iron oxide.

12) Name the compound that has the formula $CuCO_3$.

13) What is the difference between organic and inorganic chemicals?

14)* Are the following chemicals organic or inorganic? a) CH_4, b) $NaCl$, c) $CuCO_3$.

15) Why is crude oil such an important organic chemical?

16) Explain why gold occurs naturally in the ground as an element, rather than a compound.

17) Give one use of sulfur.

18) Limestone and marble are natural forms of which compound?

19) Explain how rock salt helps to make Britain's roads safer in winter.

20) Describe how you could purify a sample of rock salt in the lab.

21) Which three chemicals, important in the chemical industry, can be obtained from salt solution?

22) Which fraction produced by fractional distillation of crude oil is used as jet fuel?

23) In fractional distillation, butane is collected at the top of the fractionating column. Does it have a low or high boiling point?

24) Explain why some people think that we should stop using crude oil products like petrol as fuels.

25) The iron ore haematite is a compound of iron and which other element?

26) Write the word equation for the reduction of haematite.

27) Give one possible advantage and one possible disadvantage of living near a mine.

28) What is meant by the term 'bulk chemical'? Give two examples of bulk chemicals.

29) What are 'fine chemicals'? Give an example.

30) Give two ways you could increase the speed of a reaction in which the reactants are gases.

31) What does the steepness of a reaction rate graph tell you?

32) Give three factors which must be taken into consideration when selecting or designing a chemical manufacturing process.

*Answers on p.140.

Useful Mixtures

Chemists make loads of things that we use around the home — and many of them consist of one substance <u>finely mixed</u> with <u>another</u> (rather than pure substances). The substances used in these mixtures can be <u>solids</u>, <u>liquids</u> or <u>gases</u>. Here are <u>three types</u> of mixture...

A <u>Solution</u> *is a* <u>Substance Dissolved</u> *in a* <u>Liquid</u>

1) A solution is a substance (the <u>solute</u> — usually a solid) dispersed in a <u>liquid</u> (the <u>solvent</u>) to form a transparent liquid.

2) Some everyday examples are <u>instant coffee</u>, <u>soluble aspirin</u> and <u>bath salts</u>.

3) A solution is different from other mixtures because the bonds (see p.82) holding the solute molecules together actually <u>break</u> — the molecules <u>mix</u> completely with the molecules in the solvent. This is called <u>dissolving</u>.

4) <u>Water</u> is a very common <u>solvent</u>. In fact, the water you get from the tap already has lots of substances dissolved in it.

5) A solution can be <u>separated</u> by heating it to <u>evaporate</u> off the liquid, leaving just the solid. This is one way to get <u>salt</u> from the sea — in warm countries the Sun's heat is used to evaporate the water, leaving salt behind.

A <u>Suspension</u> *is a* <u>Cloudy Mixture</u> *of a* <u>Solid</u> *in a* <u>Liquid</u>

1) A suspension is a mixture of <u>small solid particles</u> (e.g. silt) and a <u>liquid</u> (e.g. water).

2) Unlike solutions, molecules in a suspension <u>don't mix completely</u> because the bonds between the solute molecules <u>don't break</u>. The particles in suspensions aren't small enough to stay floating around — eventually they'll <u>separate</u>, as the solid particles gradually <u>settle</u> to the bottom.

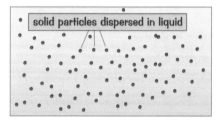
solid particles dispersed in liquid

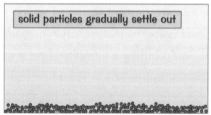
solid particles gradually settle out

3) <u>Ice cream</u> is a great example of a suspension — it's a suspension of tiny ice crystals in cream.

<u>Colloids</u> *Consist of One Substance* <u>Finely Dispersed</u> *in Another*

1) A colloid consists of <u>really tiny particles</u> of one substance (or mixture of substances) <u>finely dispersed</u> in another substance (or mixture of substances).

2) The particles can be bits of <u>solid</u>, droplets of <u>liquid</u> or bubbles of <u>gas</u>.

3) The <u>particles</u> are called the <u>dispersed phase</u>.

4) The <u>liquid</u> that contains the particles is called the <u>continuous phase</u>.

5) Colloids don't separate out because the particles are <u>so small</u>.

6) There are five types of colloid — <u>gel</u>, <u>sol</u>, <u>emulsion</u>, <u>foam</u> and <u>aerosol</u> (see next page for more).

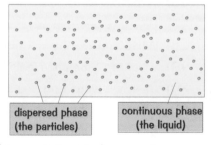
dispersed phase (the particles)   continuous phase (the liquid)

<u>Learn this page — it's the only solution...</u>

Finally an excuse to eat <u>ice cream</u> — just tell your parents it's ground-breaking scientific research into particulate bonding in <u>suspensions</u>, that stopping you from eating ice cream would be hindering your educational development. Oh yeah, and <u>jelly</u> (it's a <u>colloid</u>) — who knew revising could be so tasty...

Useful Mixtures

Colloids might seem a bit scary, but when you think about it they're not really that bad. Remember, they only contain two parts — a <u>dispersed phase</u> and a <u>continuous phase</u>.

There are *Five Types* of Colloid

1) A *Gel* is a *Jelly-Like Mixture* of a *Liquid* in a *Solid*

1) A <u>gel</u> is made from liquid dispersed in <u>tiny solid particles</u>, — the solid particles 'trap' the liquid. This means the whole thing behaves a bit <u>more like a solid</u> than a <u>liquid</u>.

2) <u>Jelly</u>, <u>hair gel</u> and some <u>toothpastes</u> are gels.

3) Some gels can <u>set</u> and become <u>hard</u>, which is why they're useful for things like <u>hair styling</u> — slap on a load of <u>hair gel</u>, sculpt it into a <u>nice quiff</u> and leave it to set. Grand.

Hair gel — mmm... gloopy   *(just don't get too carried away)*

2) A *Sol* is a *Solid* Dispersed in a *Liquid* or a *Solid*

1) Some <u>paints</u> are a mixture of <u>tiny solid pigments</u> in an <u>oily liquid base</u>. This allows the solid to be applied as a liquid.

2) <u>Stained glass</u> is an example of <u>solid particles</u> dispersed in a <u>solid</u> — the solid pigments of colour are mixed in with the glass.

3) An *Emulsion* is a *Cloudy Mixture* of a *Liquid* in *Another* Liquid

1) An <u>emulsion</u> is made from <u>tiny droplets of one liquid dispersed in another</u>, where the liquids won't properly dissolve in each other, e.g. oil and water.

2) <u>Emulsion paint</u>, <u>mayonnaise</u> and some <u>salad dressings</u> are examples of emulsions.

3) Emulsions are <u>cloudy</u>, and will <u>eventually separate</u> if left for a while. E.g. you can make salad dressing from <u>olive oil</u> and <u>vinegar</u>. You <u>shake it up</u> to make a <u>cloudy liquid</u> then drench your lettuce with it. But if you come back to it <u>tomorrow</u> lunchtime, the oil will have <u>separated out</u> and be sitting on top of the vinegar, so you'll have to <u>shake it up again</u>.

4) *Foams* Contain *Gas*

A <u>foam</u> is made of <u>tiny gas bubbles</u> dispersed in either a solid, e.g. bread, or a liquid, e.g. <u>shaving foam</u> or the head on <u>beer</u>. The presence of gas bubbles causes the foam to be <u>light</u> and <u>fluffy</u>.

5) *Aerosols* are *Liquid* in *Gas*

<u>Aerosols</u> are <u>tiny droplets of a liquid</u> dispersed in a <u>gas</u>, e.g. <u>hairspray</u> or <u>spray paint</u>. Aerosols are like a very fine mist, so you can get an <u>even coat</u> of hairspray / paint (instead of a big dollop).

Foaming at the mouth? Don't bother learning this — it's too late...

These mixtures have <u>so many uses</u> around the home that just giving them a page seems a bit unfair. But this is all you need to know, so I'll not bother your already crammed brain with any more details. For each mixture, learn the <u>structure</u>, at least <u>one use</u>, and say <u>why it's suited</u> to its use.

Chemical Bonding and Properties

By understanding the structure of materials at the <u>molecular level</u>, scientists can figure out why they have certain <u>properties</u>. They can then <u>design materials</u> with the properties we want by picking the right compounds.

Atoms in Compounds are Held Together by Bonds

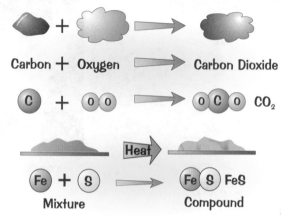

Carbon + Oxygen → Carbon Dioxide

C + O O → O C O CO$_2$

Fe + S → Fe S FeS
Mixture — Compound
(Heat)

1) Remember that compounds are formed when <u>two or more</u> elements <u>chemically react together</u>.
   For example, carbon dioxide is a <u>compound</u> formed from a <u>chemical reaction</u> between carbon and oxygen. The bonds between the oxygen atoms break and they bond to a carbon to form carbon dioxide.

2) The <u>properties</u> of a compound are <u>totally different</u> from the properties of the <u>original elements</u>.
   E.g. if iron and sulfur react to form <u>iron sulfide</u>, the compound formed is a <u>grey solid lump</u> and doesn't behave <u>anything like</u> either iron or sulfur.

3) The bonds that form can be either <u>ionic</u> or <u>covalent</u>.

Bonding Within Compounds Can be Ionic

1) In <u>ionic bonding</u>, atoms <u>lose or gain electrons</u> to form <u>charged particles</u> (called <u>ions</u>) which are then <u>strongly attracted</u> to one another — this is because of the <u>attraction</u> of <u>opposite charges</u> (positive ions will be attracted to negative ions, and vice versa).

2) <u>Ionic bonds</u> always produce <u>giant ionic structures</u>.

3) The ions form a <u>closely packed</u> regular lattice arrangement.

4) There are <u>very strong</u> chemical bonds between <u>all</u> the ions.

5) Salt is bonded together ionically. A single crystal of salt is <u>one giant ionic lattice</u>, which is why salt crystals tend to be cuboid in shape.

Ionic compounds have distinct characteristics:

1) They have high melting points and boiling points
This is due to the <u>very strong</u> chemical bonds between <u>all the ions</u> in the giant structure.

2) They dissolve to form solutions that conduct electricity
<u>When dissolved</u> the ions <u>separate</u> and are all <u>free to move</u> in the solution, which means they'll <u>carry electric current</u>.
E.g. dissolved <u>lithium salts</u> are used to make <u>rechargeable batteries</u>.

3) They conduct electricity when molten
When ionic compounds melt, the ions are free to move so they'll carry electric current.

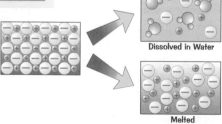

Dissolved in Water

Melted

Giant ionic structures — all over your chips...
Because they conduct electricity when they're dissolved in water, ionic compounds are used to make some types of <u>battery</u>. In the olden days, most batteries had actual liquid in, so they tended to leak all over the place. Now they've come up with a sort of <u>paste</u> that doesn't leak but still conducts. Clever.

Chemical Bonding and Properties

You never really know where you stand with ionic compounds — some are all take, take, take while others do nothing but give. Covalent compounds are a whole different kettle of fish — they're all about sharing and singing and dancing, but mostly sharing.

Bonding Within Compounds Can be Covalent

Atoms form covalent bonds by sharing electrons with other atoms, e.g. an oxygen atom shares electrons with another oxygen atom to make O_2 (oxygen gas). Covalent compounds have distinct characteristics.

1) They're Poor Conductors of Heat and Electricity

There are no free electrons in covalent bonding, so these compounds are usually poor conductors of heat and electricity. This makes them rubbish for cooking pans but great heat insulators.

Polymers also contain covalent bonding — this gives them distinct properties, and explains why they are poor conductors of heat and electricity (see page 85 for more).

2) They Have Low Density and are Often Dull in Appearance

1) All covalent compounds, solids, liquids and gases, have low densities.

2) Solid covalent compounds are often dull in appearance because they don't tend to reflect light very well. Two big exceptions to this rule are diamond (made of carbon) and quartz (made of silicon and oxygen).

3) Those That Form Small Molecules Have Low Boiling and Melting Points

1) Some compounds, e.g. chlorine, oxygen and water, contain small molecules formed by covalent bonding.

2) The forces of attraction BETWEEN these molecules are very weak.

3) This means that the melting and boiling points are very low — the molecules are easily parted from each other.

4) E.g. oxygen boils at −183 °C — that's why it's a gas at room temperature.

Very weak forces between the molecules

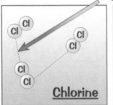
Chlorine

Oxygen

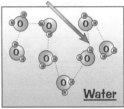
Water

4) Those That Form Giant Structures Have High Boiling and Melting Points

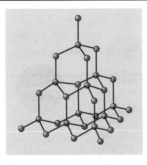

1) Covalent bonding can also form giant structures — closely packed regular lattice arrangements.

2) This means the bonds are very strong and a lot of heat energy is needed to break the bonds, giving them high boiling and melting points.

3) E.g. diamond is a giant covalent structure — it's just made of carbon and melts at 3550 °C.

Giant covalent structures — a girl's best friend...

Covalent structures are pretty great really, especially diamonds. They're the hardest material known to man (even harder than Van Damme). They are so hard that they can't be scratched by anything else, not even glass or nails — they can only be scratched by other diamonds. Nifty.

Ceramics

Every object that's built serves some kind of <u>purpose</u> — whether it's something small like a fridge or something monstrous like a tower block. The materials used in these objects must have the <u>right properties</u> to suit the purpose. There's a whole range of materials that we could use, like <u>ceramics</u>, <u>metals</u>, <u>composites</u> and <u>polymers</u> — they all have their own <u>distinct properties</u>.

Ceramics are Materials Made by Heating

1) <u>POTTERY</u> and <u>PORCELAIN</u> — made by <u>heating clay</u>. When it's <u>wet</u> clay can be <u>moulded</u> into any shape you like. '<u>Firing</u>' it in a hot oven (a kiln) makes it turn <u>hard</u> and keep its <u>shape</u>. It can be <u>glazed</u> to add colours or patterns.

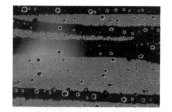

2) <u>GLASS</u> — made by <u>heating sand</u> with other chemicals. It's <u>transparent</u>, can be made <u>different colours</u> and can be made into <u>any shape</u>, including big flat sheets.

3) <u>CEMENT</u> — made by <u>heating limestone</u> with <u>clay</u>. When you mix cement with water it becomes runny and then sets hard. Cement is used to <u>stick bricks</u> and <u>stone</u> together, and to make <u>concrete</u>.

Ceramics are Hard-Wearing, but Brittle

USEFUL PROPERTIES OF CERAMICS:
1) <u>Hard-wearing</u> — they don't scratch easily.
2) <u>High melting point</u> — they are <u>heat-</u> and <u>fire-resistant</u>.
3) <u>Waterproof</u> and <u>smooth</u> — easily <u>cleaned</u> and <u>hygienic</u>.
4) <u>Inert</u> — they don't <u>corrode</u> or <u>react</u> with chemicals.
5) <u>Electrical insulators</u> — ceramics <u>are poor conductors of electricity</u>.
6) <u>Attractive appearance</u> — come in <u>different colours</u> and <u>patterns</u>.

A NOT-SO-USEFUL PROPERTY:
They're <u>brittle</u> — they aren't very <u>flexible</u> and <u>break easily</u>.

They're Useful for Building Houses and Serving Food

These properties make ceramics useful for loads of building materials and household things...

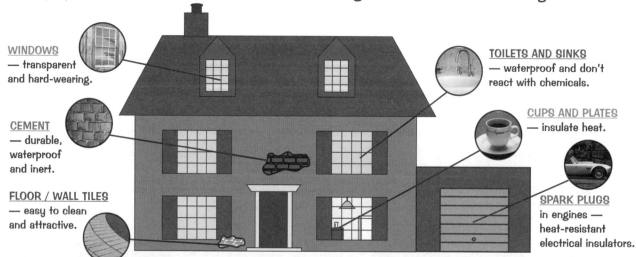

WINDOWS — transparent and hard-wearing.

CEMENT — durable, waterproof and inert.

FLOOR / WALL TILES — easy to clean and attractive.

TOILETS AND SINKS — waterproof and don't react with chemicals.

CUPS AND PLATES — insulate heat.

SPARK PLUGS in engines — heat-resistant electrical insulators.

If they weren't inanimate they'd be my china plate...

If you don't get it ask a cockney.

Ceramics don't burn, melt, rot, rust or get eaten by termites, which is handy really. The only downside is they're <u>easily broken</u> or smashed — so keep your cricket balls and clumsy hands away from them.

Polymers

The plastics we use in day-to-day life are all polymers. Plastics are amazingly useful things — you can keep things in them, wear them, carry things in them or hide under them — just don't eat them.

Polymers' Properties Decide What They're Used For

Different polymers have different physical properties — some are strong, others are stretchy, some are easily moulded, and so on. These different physical properties make them suited for different uses.

1) FLEXIBILITY — some polymers are pretty bendy and stretchy. Poly(ethene) is a flexible polymer — it's used to make plastic bags and squeezy bottles. Nylon is a flexible polymer used to make tights and toothbrush bristles.

2) BEHAVIOUR ON HEATING — some polymers (e.g. poly(ethene) and nylon) have a low melting point. They melt when heated, so they're no good for anything that'll get very hot, like a kettle. Some polymers are heat-resistant, e.g. melamine is used to make kitchen utensils and plates. When melted, polymers can easily be moulded into different shapes.

3) POOR CONDUCTORS OF HEAT — polymers generally don't transfer heat well — they're good insulators, e.g. they're great for things like coffee cups and pan handles. (Polymers are great for pan handles because they don't allow the heat from the pan to get to your hands.)

4) POOR CONDUCTORS OF ELECTRICITY — polymers don't allow an electric current to flow through them. They can be used as electric wire insulation — the electricity is trapped in, so it can only flow down the wire, making them safe for you to handle. The cases of many appliances (e.g. hairdriers) are plastic for the same reason.

So when you're making a product, you need to pick your polymer carefully. It's pointless trying to make a kettle out of a plastic that melts at 50 °C (all you'd end up with is a messy kitchen, a burnt hand and no brew). You'd also have a bit of difficulty trying to wear clothes made of brittle, unbendy plastic — think about what job you need a plastic to do and what properties it needs to do it.

Poor conductors have plastic batons...

Plastics sound great but they're pretty hard things to get rid of — they aren't biodegradable, so they don't rot. This is great until you need to get rid of your plastic. Burning them damages the environment and if you throw them away they end up in landfill sites — and could be there for thousands of years. The best thing to do is recycle them. Some clever scientists have invented a biodegradable plastic bag. But this doesn't solve the problem of all the millions already hanging around on our planet.

Metals

Just like polymers and ceramics, different metals have different properties. And I'm sure you can guess by now... their uses depend on their properties.

Different Metals Have Different Properties

Generally speaking, most metals have these properties:
- Strong — they can take a lot of weight.
- Tough and resistant to corrosion — they don't wear easily.
- Good conductors of heat and electricity.
- High density and hard.
- High melting point.

But these properties vary in different metals:

Aluminium
1) For a metal it's lightweight — it has a relatively low density.
2) Resistant to corrosion.
3) Can be easily moulded.

So, aluminium is often used for window frames.

Iron
1) Strong — it can take a lot of weight before it bends or breaks.
2) Cheap to produce.
3) High density — it weighs a lot.
4) Hard and tough — will last a long time.

Iron is used for its strength as a support material. But before it can be used outside, it has to be coated (e.g. with paint or plastic) to stop it rusting.

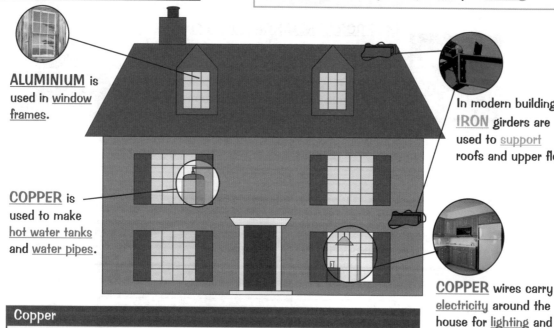

ALUMINIUM is used in window frames.

In modern buildings, IRON girders are used to support roofs and upper floors.

COPPER is used to make hot water tanks and water pipes.

COPPER wires carry electricity around the house for lighting and electrical appliances.

Copper
1) Malleable and ductile — it can be beaten into sheets and rolled up to make pipes, and can be drawn out into long wires.
2) Excellent conductor of electricity.
3) High melting point — it can cope well with high temperatures.
4) Doesn't corrode with water.

Copper is ideal for water pipes and hot water storage. It doesn't corrode like iron, or melt like some plastics. Very pure copper is used to make the wires in electrical circuits — it's one of the best electrical conductors around.

My mum keeps telling me to learn some uses of iron...

...or was it the iron? Anyway — you wouldn't want to use iron to mend gaps in your roof. A bit of rain and all you'd be left with is a little pile of rust and a wet carpet. You need to match uses to properties.

Metal Recycling and Composites

Metals are a <u>finite resource</u> — that means one day they're going to <u>run out</u>. Here's a crazy idea that might just catch on — why not <u>recycle</u> them.

Recycling Metal **Has** Advantages **and** Disadvantages

ADVANTAGES

1) Recycling metals only uses a <u>small fraction</u> of the <u>energy</u> needed to mine and extract new metal. So, <u>less fossil fuels</u> are used (which is good news for the environment) and recycled metal should be <u>cheaper</u> to buy.

2) There's a <u>finite</u> amount of each metal in the Earth — they will run out eventually. Recycling <u>conserves</u> these <u>resources</u>.

3) Recycling metal cuts down on the amount of <u>rubbish</u> that gets sent to <u>landfill</u>. Landfill takes up <u>space</u> and <u>pollutes</u> the local environment. E.g. if all the aluminium cans in the UK were recycled, there'd be 14 million fewer full dustbins each year.

DISADVANTAGES

1) It can be very <u>expensive</u> to <u>purify</u> recycled metals, and many recycled metals are <u>impure</u> (depending on where they came from). E.g. recycled copper is usually impure but electrical wires must be made from very pure copper.

2) Recycling can be very <u>labour-intensive</u> — e.g. when recycling a car, all the <u>metal</u> needs to be <u>separated</u> from the plastic bits first, which takes ages.

Composites Combine **the** Properties **of Two or More Materials**

Manufacturers and designers can't always find one material that has all the properties they need. A mixture of <u>two materials</u> often provides the solution — these mixtures are called <u>COMPOSITES</u>. They combine the properties of the two materials.

Two examples of composites are:

<u>REINFORCED CONCRETE</u>

This is <u>concrete</u> made <u>stronger</u> by adding <u>rods</u> of <u>metal</u> — usually <u>steel</u>. The concrete provides the basic <u>strength</u> while the metal stops the whole thing <u>bending</u> or <u>stretching</u>. This composite is very strong and durable, making it an ideal material for constructing <u>buildings</u>.

<u>GRP — GLASS-REINFORCED PLASTIC</u>

GRP is <u>plastic reinforced</u> by <u>small fibres</u> of <u>glass</u>. This makes it <u>stronger</u> than <u>plastic</u> but not as <u>brittle</u> as <u>glass</u>. It can also be <u>moulded</u> into different shapes. It's used to make things like <u>baths</u> as well as the bodies of <u>aeroplanes</u>.

Two materials went on holiday — they stayed on a compo-site...

Don't forget that the <u>properties</u> of <u>composites</u> come from the properties of their <u>components</u>, e.g. mint choc chip ice cream is so tasty because it combines crunchy chocolate bits with minty fresh ice cream. Mmmm.

Developing New Materials

New materials are constantly being explored by scientists so they can find the best materials for... well, pretty much anything and everything. Before a material can be sold it has to go through several stages to make sure it's totally suitable. Materials for air- and spacecraft are a major area of research...

There are Seven Main Steps in Producing New Materials

1 DEVELOPMENT

The properties that the new material must have need to be worked out — these depend on what the material will be used for. Scientists pick a few different materials with the right qualities to compare. Suppose a new composite material was needed for a spacecraft shell, — materials that are lightweight but strong, have a very high melting point and are hard-wearing would be chosen for development.

2 TESTING

Once materials have been chosen, they have to be tested under different conditions to see just how suitable they are. So the composite for the spacecraft would be tested under different pressures, at different temperatures and under different stresses.

3 SPECIFICATION MATCHING

This stage makes sure that the material does exactly what you need it to do and is completely suitable in every single way. Specification matching makes sure that the composite meets all the requirements for space travel but also takes into account price and availability.

4 DEVELOPMENT OF NECESSARY COMPONENT MATERIALS, e.g. glues.
Other materials might be needed to make the whole thing work —
e.g. the spacecraft composite might require a special protective coating.

5 DESIGN OF MANUFACTURING PROCESS
Scientists need to figure out how they're going to make the material. They work out how long it'll take to manufacture and what special machinery will be needed.

6 SAFETY
Scientists have to make sure that everything is safe to work with — not only the material but also the equipment used to make it.

7 ENVIRONMENTAL ISSUES
Everyone developing new materials has to make sure they follow all the rules about recycling, disposing of and making the material so as not to damage the environment.

Even our joke material is subject to these seven steps...

Every new material has to go through all these stages in turn — not only materials for spacecraft. Each step is really important to make sure that the material is just right for the job.

Section 2.4 — Chemical and Material Behaviour

Matching Properties and Uses

You may be asked to interpret data about the physical properties of materials in the exam. What a coincidence — here's some data all about metals. Remember this is about interpreting data — you don't have to learn it, you just have to be able to do it. Phew, that's a load off my mind.

You Might be Asked to Find the Physical Properties...

Here's an article about the cost of metals, a chart showing melting points and a table showing some other exciting properties of metals.

The Cost of Metals

Metals need to be extracted and processed before they can be used, which often affects the cost of the metal. Iron is the most widely used and cheapest metal and is the second most abundant metal in the Earth's crust. Copper is more expensive, it's not as abundant and it takes a lot of energy to purify. Aluminium is the most abundant metal in the Earth's crust and is second only to iron as the most widely used metal. It's abundance means it's cheaper than copper. Lead is the least abundant of the four metals but is relatively cheap.

METAL	ELECTRICAL CONDUCTIVITY	DENSITY (how heavy it is)	STRENGTH
Copper	Good ↑	8.96 g/cm³	Strong but quite malleable
Aluminium		2.7 g/cm³	Strong but quite malleable
Iron		7.86 g/cm³	Very strong, not very malleable
Lead	Poor ↓	11.34 g/cm³	Soft and malleable

You might face questions like ...

1) **What is the approximate melting point of aluminium?**
To find this look at the bar chart and find the bar representing aluminium.
Reading off the graph, your answer's 700 °C.

2) **What is the density of iron?**
You'll need to use the table to find this. Reading down the density column, iron has a density of 2.7 g/cm³.

3) **Which is the cheapest metal?**
This isn't in the graph or the table so you'll need to have a quick read of the article — now you've done that you'll know it's iron.

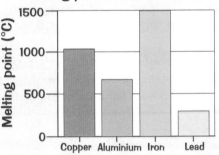

A bar chart showing the approximate melting points of four metals

...or Match the Properties with Uses

Here's a question about metals (but it could quite easily be about ceramics or composites or whatever): Using the data above pick a metal that could be used for: 1) cooking pans, 2) electrical wire.
Have a go yourself before you look at my answer below, and remember, give reasons for your choice.

COOKING PANS

For pans you couldn't use lead, as its melting point is too low — you don't want the pan melting all over the place before your sausages are cooked. But iron is ideal — it's got a high melting point, which means it can withstand lots of heating. It's also cheap and abundant.

ELECTRICAL WIRE

For electrical wiring you can't use iron or lead as they're not great at conducting electricity. Copper on the other hand is a great conductor of electricity. It's also malleable, making it easy to draw out into wires.

Phwoar — look at the physical properties on that...

Questions like these could well come up in the exam. Hopefully this page wasn't too hard — all the information you need to answer the questions is there, you just need to be able to find and interpret it.

Matching Properties and Uses

The <u>materials</u> you choose to use when making a <u>product</u> are <u>very important</u> — <u>think carefully</u> about which material is <u>best suited</u> for the selected job, because if you don't your product <u>might not work</u>.

Consider the Product Before Choosing Your Materials

When you make a product (e.g. a shed or a block of flats) you need to make sure you know what <u>properties</u> are <u>important</u>. This information might be given to you in the form of a <u>design specification</u> — a list of <u>conditions</u> you need to meet in order for the <u>product to work well</u>. From this you can choose the materials that <u>best fit</u> your needs. Here's an example:

1) You need to design a <u>garden shed</u> to house a collection of <u>gnomes</u> during the winter. This is the design specification you're given.

<u>DESIGN SPECIFICATION: GARDEN SHED FOR GNOMES</u>

1) <u>Strong</u> and <u>sturdy</u> (may need extra reinforcements)
2) <u>Solid</u> base / foundation
3) <u>Waterproof</u> (you don't want your precious gnomes getting wet)
4) <u>Cheap</u>
5) <u>Transparent</u> windows (your gnomes need a good view to stop them getting bored)
6) <u>Secure roof</u>
7) <u>Entrance</u>

2) There are loads of materials to choose from — <u>metals</u>, <u>polymers</u>, <u>ceramics</u> and <u>composites</u>. Think about what materials have the <u>right properties</u>.

3) Here are a few examples of the materials you might pick for the shed, along with the <u>reasons</u> for choosing them:

The <u>roof</u> needs to be <u>waterproof</u> — ceramics, metals and polymers are all waterproof but ceramics would be too heavy so a <u>light metal</u> or <u>plastic</u> roof would be perfect.

To help <u>strengthen</u> the structure you could use <u>metal</u> supports because metal is <u>strong</u>.

The windows need to be <u>transparent</u> and <u>durable</u> (to withstand the weather). <u>Glass</u> or <u>clear plastic</u> both fit the bill as they're both transparent and hard-wearing.

<u>Fixtures</u> and <u>fittings</u> (like door handles) need to be <u>durable</u> and fairly <u>resistant</u> to <u>corrosion</u>. Plastic has these <u>properties</u> so would be ideal.

The walls need to be <u>strong</u>, <u>sturdy</u>, <u>cheap</u> and <u>durable</u> — a <u>light metal</u> or <u>plastic</u> would be good because they have these properties.

You need a <u>strong</u> base — <u>concrete</u> would be a good choice as it's strong, can be poured into any shape (and it's cheap).

A paper shed — you should've gnome better...

So, find the properties you need to make your product work, then pick materials with the <u>exact same</u> properties — not hard really, if you use some <u>common sense</u>. Don't forget — give <u>reasons</u> for your <u>choice</u>.

Revision Summary for Section 2.4

So you reckon you'll be able to build a house from scratch and fit it out with everything the modern house needs, and you'll be able to pick the right materials to do it all with, in a safe and environmentally friendly way? Prove it.

1) What is a solution?
2) What is a suspension?
3) Describe the difference between a solution and a suspension.
4) What is a colloid?
5) Describe the dispersed phase and the continuous phase in a sol.
6) Which type of colloid is made up of a gas dispersed in a liquid?
7) Describe what happens in ionic bonding.
8) State three characteristic properties of ionic compounds.
9) Describe what happens in covalent bonding.
10) Why are covalent compounds poor conductors of electricity?
11) Why do some covalent compounds have low boiling and melting points?
12) What is cement made of?
13) Name four useful properties of ceramics.
14) Name four uses of ceramics in the home.
15) State four different properties of polymers.
16) Describe one use of nylon.
17) Name a polymer that doesn't melt on heating.
18) Why are polymers good for pan handles?
19) State three general properties of metals.
20) Why is aluminium good for window frames?
21) What makes iron a good support material?
22) Name two advantages and two disadvantages of recycling metal.
23) What is a composite?
24) What are the components of reinforced concrete?
25) Why is glass-reinforced plastic sometimes used instead of normal plastic?
26) Why do new materials need to be tested?
27) Describe the seven main steps in producing a new material.
28) Why is specification matching important?
29)*Suggest a material you might use for:
   a) a frying pan base,
   b) structural reinforcements in an office block,
   c) a toilet,
   d) a coffee pot,
   e) electrical wiring,
   f) plates.

* Answers on page 140.

Fossil Fuels

Fossil fuels currently provide most of the <u>energy</u> we use, e.g. to make <u>electricity</u>, power our <u>cars</u>, <u>heat</u> our homes... I don't know what we'd do <u>without</u> them. The problem is, one day we may have to — it won't be long before we all have giant hamster wheels in our houses to make electricity just so we can watch Corrie.

The <u>Energy</u> in Fossil Fuels <u>Came</u> from the <u>Sun</u>

1) Fossil fuels include <u>coal</u>, <u>crude oil</u> and <u>natural gas</u>. They formed over <u>millions</u> of years from the <u>remains</u> of dead <u>plants</u> and <u>animals</u> (which originally got all their <u>energy</u> from the <u>Sun</u>).

2) They're a useful source of <u>energy</u> (see p.97 for how they're used to generate electricity) — energy is <u>released</u> from fossil fuels by <u>burning</u> them with <u>oxygen</u>.

an oil well

3) Chemicals from <u>crude oil</u> are also used to make lots of different <u>consumer products</u>, e.g. <u>plastics</u>, <u>medicines</u>, <u>textiles</u>, <u>make-up</u>, <u>dyes</u>, <u>paints</u>... it's all very useful stuff.

4) And there's one other important thing you need to know about fossil fuels:

> Fossil fuels are <u>NON-RENEWABLE</u> — they can't be replaced. That means there's a <u>limited supply</u> of fossil fuels that will <u>run out</u> one day. Some other energy sources are <u>renewable</u> — they will <u>never</u> run out (see p.94-95). It makes sense to try to use <u>more</u> of these now, <u>before</u> we run out of fuel.

There Are Things to <u>Think About</u> <u>When</u> <u>Choosing Fossil Fuels</u>

There are a few different <u>factors</u> you need to think about when you're <u>choosing</u> a fuel:

1) `ENERGY VALUE` — of the fossil fuels, <u>gas</u> provides the most energy per kg, and <u>coal</u> the least.

2) `SHORT-TERM AVAILABILITY` — all the fossil fuels are <u>readily available</u> now, although there are fears that the demand could soon start to <u>overtake</u> the available supply.

3) `LONG-TERM AVAILABILITY` — bad news. Many scientists think fossil fuels may run out completely in the next <u>100 years</u>. There's more <u>coal</u> around than oil or gas, but a lot of it's hard to get to.

4) `STORAGE` — oil and coal are fairly <u>easy</u> to handle, transport and store (although coal is a bit bulky). Gas is <u>trickier</u> — it's usually transported to homes or power plants by <u>pipeline</u>.

5) `COST` — All three fossil fuels are currently quite <u>cheap</u>, with <u>coal</u> being the cheapest. However, as reserves decrease and demand continues to increase, they will get more and more <u>expensive</u>.

6) `POLLUTION` — more <u>bad news</u> (see below). All three are polluting, but <u>coal</u> causes the <u>most</u> pollution.

7) `EASE OF USE` — all three <u>burn easily</u> in oxygen to release energy.

Using Fossil Fuels Can Cause *Environmental Problems*

1) <u>Fossil fuels</u> release CO_2 when they're burnt. For the same amount of energy produced, coal releases the most, followed by oil then gas. This CO_2 all adds to the <u>greenhouse effect</u> (see p.112) which could contribute to <u>climate change</u>.

2) Burning coal and oil releases <u>sulfur dioxide</u> (because they contain sulfur impurities) which causes <u>acid rain</u>. This can be reduced by removing sulfur <u>before</u> the fuel is burnt, or by cleaning up <u>emissions</u>.

3) <u>Coal mining</u> makes a <u>mess</u> of the <u>landscape</u> and can pollute nearby rivers and lakes.

4) <u>Oil spillages</u> cause <u>serious environmental problems</u>. We try to avoid them, but they'll always happen.

Revising fossil fuels — you know the drill...

Just think, next time you put the kettle on — the energy could well have come from some <u>prehistoric animal</u>, that ate a <u>plant</u>, that <u>converted light energy</u> from the Sun, and now you're using it to make a brew — pretty amazing I think. Offer up a small thank you to the T-rex or whatever as you sip.

Alternative Energy Resources

In addition to <u>renewable sources</u> there's also a <u>non-renewable</u> alternative to fossil fuels — <u>nuclear power</u>. It's <u>relatively clean</u> and the fuel is <u>cheap</u> and <u>readily available</u>. Despite all this, there are those who <u>disagree</u> with using nuclear power because of its potential impact on the environment.

Nuclear Energy Comes from the Nuclei of Atoms

1) <u>Nuclear power stations</u> are powered by <u>nuclear reactors</u>.
2) In a nuclear reactor, atoms of nuclear fuel are <u>split up</u> — this is known as <u>nuclear fission</u> and it <u>releases heat energy</u>.
3) This energy is used to <u>heat water</u> in order to drive a <u>steam turbine</u> and generate electricity (see p.97).
4) The "<u>fuel</u>" is usually either <u>uranium</u> or <u>plutonium</u> (or both). These are <u>radioactive elements</u> — their atoms have unstable nuclei that emit <u>radiation</u> (energy, basically).
5) <u>1 kg of uranium</u> can give out as much heat in a nuclear reaction as burning <u>2 000 000 kg of coal</u>.

Nuclear Power Stations Don't Emit CO_2...

1) The biggest problems with <u>fossil fuels</u> are that they give out lots of <u>carbon dioxide</u> as they burn, and they're <u>running out</u> fairly rapidly (p.92).
2) Nuclear power doesn't produce <u>as much CO_2</u> (only the CO_2 released during mining, processing and transporting the fuel) — but there are other <u>environmental problems</u> (see below).
3) Nuclear power is <u>non-renewable</u> but there's enough uranium to last <u>a long time</u>, making it a more <u>long-term solution</u> than fossil fuels.

...but Radioactive Waste is an Environmental Risk

<u>Nuclear power</u> is <u>relatively clean</u> but the <u>nuclear waste</u> is very <u>dangerous</u> and difficult to <u>dispose of</u>.

1) Nuclear power produces <u>radioactive waste</u> — this can emit dangerous radiation for <u>thousands of years</u>. This radiation could make anyone exposed to it ill and could even kill them, which is why nuclear waste needs to be <u>stored safely</u>.
2) Storage depends on the <u>type of waste</u> — some types of waste are <u>more dangerous</u> than others. E.g. <u>gloves</u> or <u>clothing</u> used in a lab are fairly safe, whereas <u>used fuel rods</u> have to be <u>cooled in water</u> before being <u>sealed in glass blocks</u> and <u>buried underground</u>.

When they're working <u>normally</u>, nuclear reactors are very <u>safe and clean</u> (in terms of polluting gases) but nuclear power always carries the <u>risk</u> of a <u>major catastrophe</u> — like the <u>Chernobyl disaster</u>.

1) In 1986 technicians at a reactor in Chernobyl turned off the <u>safety devices</u> to test the reactor.
2) The reactor <u>overheated</u> and <u>exploded</u>. Large amounts of <u>radioactive material</u> were released into the <u>atmosphere</u> and spread across Europe.
3) Many people <u>died</u> and many more were made <u>ill</u>. Many areas around Chernobyl are still <u>contaminated</u>.

Nuclear <u>fuel</u> (i.e. uranium) is <u>relatively cheap</u>, but the <u>overall cost</u> of nuclear power is <u>high</u> (because of the cost of building and knocking down the <u>power plant</u> and <u>disposal</u> of waste). Plants also need to be well <u>maintained</u> — <u>accidents</u> are more likely to happen as the reactors become <u>older</u> and <u>less efficient</u>.

Nuclear — think that's the name of my face wash...

With <u>decreasing</u> supplies of <u>fossil fuels</u>, and <u>renewables</u> unable to meet all our <u>energy needs</u>, <u>nuclear power</u> could be an important option in the <u>future</u>. That doesn't mean everyone has to like it though — many people <u>oppose</u> nuclear power because of the possibility of <u>environmental damage</u>.

Alternative Energy Resources

The renewable energy resources you need to know about are:

1) Wind   2) Hydroelectric   3) Solar   4) Wave   5) Tidal   6) Biomass and biofuel

- These will never run out.
- Most of them do damage the environment, but in less nasty ways than non-renewables.
- But they don't all provide much energy and some are unreliable because they depend on the weather.

Wind Power — Lots of Little Wind Turbines

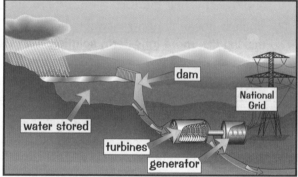

1) A wind farm is just lots of wind turbines. They're put up in exposed places like on moors or near coasts where there's lots of wind.

2) The wind turns the blades, which turn a generator inside the turbine.

3) There's no pollution (except for a little bit when they're made).

4) However, there are a few problems. You need about 1500 wind turbines to replace one coal-fired power station. They affect the view and can be noisy, which can be annoying for people living nearby. There's no power when the wind stops, and it's impossible to increase supply when there's extra demand.

Hydroelectricity — Reliable but Damages the Environment

1) Hydroelectric power usually requires the flooding of a valley by building a big dam.

2) Water is trapped behind the dam and allowed out through turbines when electricity is needed.

3) There's no pollution, but there is a big impact on the environment due to the flooding of the valley and possible loss of habitat for some species. The reservoirs can also look very unsightly when they dry up.

dam

National Grid

water stored

turbines

generator

4) A big advantage is immediate response to increased demand, and there's no problem with reliability except in times of drought.

5) Initial costs are high, but there's no fuel and minimal running costs.

Solar Energy — Expensive but No Environmental Damage

1) Solar cells generate electric currents directly from sunlight.

2) They're often used in remote places where there's not much choice, e.g. the Australian outback.

3) There's no pollution. (Although it takes quite a lot of energy to manufacture a solar cell in the first place.)

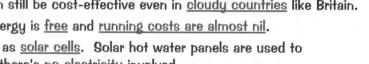

Sunlight   Electric current

Solar cell   Electrical components

4) In sunny countries solar power is a very reliable source of energy — but only in the daytime. It can still be cost-effective even in cloudy countries like Britain.

5) Initial costs are high but after that the energy is free and running costs are almost nil.

6) Solar hot water panels are NOT the same as solar cells. Solar hot water panels are used to directly heat water for household use — there's no electricity involved.

The hydroelectric power you're supplying — it's electrifying...

The big advantage of renewable fuels is that they don't release CO_2. But like all good things in life, they have a number of disadvantages, such as unreliability and environmental damage. The examiners could ask you to compare a renewable resource with fossil fuels — make sure you know all the pros and cons.

Alternative Energy Resources

At the moment about 4% of the UK's electricity is generated from renewable sources, and the Government hopes to increase this to 10% by 2010. Coming up are the remaining three you need to know about...

Wave Power — Lots of Little Wave Converters

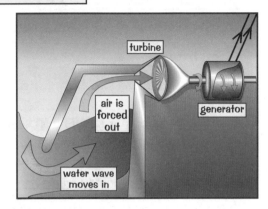

1) Wave-powered generators can be located around the coast.

2) Waves provide an up and down motion — this movement can be used to drive a generator.

3) There's no pollution. The main problems are spoiling the view and being a hazard to boats.

4) They're a fairly unreliable source of power though, since waves tend to die down when the wind drops.

5) Initial costs are high but there are no fuel costs and minimal running costs.

Tidal Barrages — Using the Sun and Moon's Gravity

1) Tidal barrages are big dams built across river estuaries, with turbines in them.

2) As the tide comes in it fills up the estuary to a height of several metres. This water can then be allowed out through turbines at a controlled speed. It also drives the turbines on the way in.

3) There's no pollution. The main problems are preventing free access by boats, spoiling the view and altering the habitat of the wildlife, e.g. wading birds, sea creatures and beasties who live in the sand.

4) Tides are pretty reliable in the sense that they happen twice a day without fail. The only drawback is that the height of the tide is variable — and lower tides provide less energy.

5) Initial costs are moderately high but there are no fuel costs and minimal running costs. Even though it can only be used in a few of the most suitable estuaries, tidal power has the potential to generate a significant amount of energy.

Biofuels Are Made From Once-living Material (Biomass)

1) Biomass is the general term for all manner of organic 'stuff' that can be burnt to give energy. It can be anything from farm waste, animal manure and some landfill rubbish to wood from specially-grown forests.

2) The material can be burnt in power stations to drive turbines and produce electricity.

3) Sometimes it's fermented to produce other fuels, called biofuels, such as 'biogas' (usually methane) or ethanol. Ethanol can be used to run cars, either mixed with petrol or by itself in special engines.

4) Fuel costs and set-up costs are generally low, since the fuel is usually waste, and the fuels can often be burnt in converted coal-fired power stations.

5) This process makes use of waste material, which could be great news for our already overflowing landfill sites. But the downside of using unsorted landfill rubbish, rather than just plant and animal waste, is that burning it can release nasty gases like sulfur dioxide and nitrogen oxides.

Renewable energy — wave goodbye to fossil fuels...

It's really important that you appreciate the big big differences between tidal power and wave power. Yes, they both involve salty sea water, but the similarities start and end there.

Energy Transfer

Energy from <u>any source</u>, be it fossil fuel, nuclear or solar, is only useful if it can be <u>converted</u> into other forms. There are lots of different <u>types of energy</u> that are <u>useful</u> for lots of different things.

Learn These *Five Types of Energy*

You should know all of these <u>well enough</u> by now to list them <u>from memory</u>, including the examples:

1) <u>ELECTRICAL</u> energy .... wherever a <u>current</u> flows (see p.102).
2) <u>LIGHT</u> energy .... from the <u>Sun</u>, <u>light bulbs</u>, etc.
3) <u>SOUND</u> energy .... from <u>loudspeakers</u> or anything <u>noisy</u>.
4) <u>KINETIC</u> energy or <u>MOVEMENT</u> energy .... anything that's <u>moving</u> has it.
5) <u>THERMAL</u> energy or <u>HEAT</u> energy .... <u>flows</u> from <u>hot objects</u> to colder ones.

Here are some <u>useful energy transfers</u> in action:

ELECTRICAL DEVICES CONVERT ELECTRICAL ENERGY INTO SOUND, LIGHT, HEAT, ETC.

(and a bit of wasted heat)

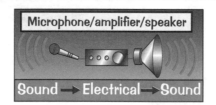

Microphone/amplifier/speaker

Sound → Electrical → Sound

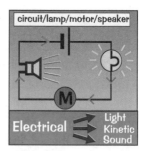

circuit/lamp/motor/speaker

Electrical → Light Kinetic Sound

And of course, that <u>electrical energy</u> came from an <u>energy transfer</u> that was prepared earlier:

ELECTRICITY GENERATION ALWAYS INVOLVES CONVERTING OTHER FORMS OF ENERGY INTO ELECTRICAL ENERGY.

(and of course — there's a bit of wasted heat)

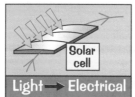

Solar cell

Light → Electrical

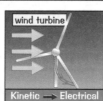

wind turbine

Kinetic → Electrical

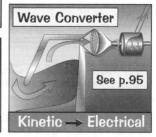

Wave Converter

See p.95

Kinetic → Electrical

The *Principle of Conservation of Energy Can be Stated Like This:*

This is one of the most important <u>laws of physics</u>, so learn it well.

ENERGY CAN NEVER BE <u>CREATED NOR DESTROYED</u> — IT'S ONLY EVER <u>CONVERTED</u> FROM ONE FORM TO ANOTHER.

Another <u>important principle</u> which you need to <u>learn</u> is this one:

Energy is <u>only useful</u> when it can be <u>converted</u> from one form to another.

Energy can't be created or destroyed — only talked about a lot...*

There are <u>other</u> types of energy too — like <u>chemical</u> energy (in food and fuel and stuff) and <u>elastic</u> <u>potential</u> energy and <u>gravitational potential</u> energy. But they're <u>not</u> on the specification, so don't worry.

Generating Electricity

One of the most useful things you can do with energy from fuels (or wind turbines or whatever) is to convert it into <u>electricity</u>, because this can then be converted so easily into any <u>other type</u> of energy you might need.

Most Power Stations Use Steam to Drive a Turbine

1) <u>Most</u> electricity we use is <u>generated</u> from <u>non-renewable</u> energy sources (<u>fossil fuels</u> and <u>nuclear</u>).

2) <u>Big power stations</u> all work on the same principles — using <u>steam</u> to <u>turn</u> a <u>turbine</u>.

3) The big <u>difference</u> between power stations is their <u>boilers</u>. The boiler in a <u>coal-powered</u> power station will be very different from the reactor in a <u>nuclear</u> power station.

4) There are <u>three basic stages</u> to generating electricity in a typical power station:

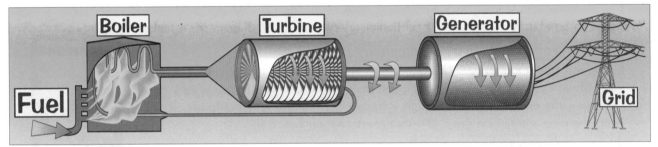

 **Chemical energy**

1) Fuel is burnt and the <u>heat given out</u> is used to <u>boil water</u>.

 Heat energy

2) <u>Steam</u> from the boiling water is used to <u>turn a turbine</u>.

 Kinetic energy

3) The <u>turbine rotates</u> a <u>generator</u> to <u>create electricity</u>.

 **Electrical energy**

5) Before becoming <u>electrical energy</u>, the <u>chemical energy</u> of the fuel is converted into two other types of energy (<u>heat energy</u> and <u>kinetic energy</u>).

6) This process <u>isn't very efficient</u> (see p.99) because every time the energy is <u>converted</u> you <u>lose a bit</u>. In fact, coal-fired power stations convert less than 40% of the energy in the fuel into electricity.

7) This means that electricity can be quite <u>expensive</u> to generate (and so expensive to buy).

Electricity Gets Around *via the* National Grid

The <u>National Grid</u> is the <u>network</u> of pylons and cables that covers <u>the whole of Britain</u>, getting electricity to homes everywhere.
Whoever you pay for your electricity, it's the National Grid that gets it to you.

1) The <u>National Grid</u> takes electrical energy from the <u>power stations</u> to everywhere it's needed, like <u>homes</u> and <u>industry</u>.

2) It means power can be <u>generated</u> anywhere on the grid, and then be <u>supplied</u> to anywhere else on the grid.

S-team drives a turbine, the A-team drove a van...

The way we make electricity today uses the same idea as <u>steam engines</u> — heating <u>water</u> to make <u>steam</u> and then using steam to produce <u>kinetic energy</u>. Steam engines were invented way before you and I were born, in the 17th century. It's amazing that the same <u>principle</u> is still being used today — bet you can't think of many other things that have lasted that long (apart from maybe forks and Bruce Forsyth).

Energy in the Home

Electricity Can be Converted into Lots of Forms of Energy:

Electrical energy is very useful because devices can be used to convert it into many useful forms of energy at the touch of a button:
- LIGHT ENERGY, e.g. light bulbs, TVs.
- HEAT ENERGY, e.g. kettles, toasters, fan heaters.
- KINETIC (MOVING) ENERGY, e.g. anything with an electric motor in it.
- SOUND ENERGY, e.g. stereos, MP3 players, TVs.

Different Energy Sources are Useful for Different Things

Energy doesn't just come in the form of mains electricity — some homes use different sources of energy, such as natural gas, oil, wood or coal. And then there's battery power, of course. Each source contains energy that can be changed into a form of energy that we need. You need to be able to explain why a particular energy source is chosen for a task:

1) **MAINS ELECTRICITY — VERY CONVENIENT:**
Mains electricity can provide enough power for all your domestic appliances, even those that need loads of power, like dishwashers. The main drawback is safety — the mains supply is at high voltage (230 V) and an electric shock from the mains could kill you. It's also pretty expensive.

2) **NATURAL GAS — CHEAPER for HEATING:**

mains gas   bottled gas

Mains gas is used in many homes for heating and cooking. It's often cheaper than electricity. It burns efficiently and has few impurities — it's a clean fuel. But you can only use it to provide heat — it won't power the TV, for example. You can also get natural gas in bottles if there's no access to mains gas, but it's a bit more expensive.

3) **OIL — CONVENIENT for HEATING in REMOTE AREAS:**
This is used in some homes instead of gas for heating and cooking. As it's a liquid, it's easier to store than natural gas and is often used in rural areas where it's not possible to lay gas pipelines to homes.

oil tank

4) **SOLID FUELS — CHEAP and CHEERFUL:**

Solid fuels like coal and wood are used for similar reasons to oil, although they're bulkier and so not as convenient to store. They're cheap, and some people like the look of a nice open coal or wood fire.

5) **BATTERIES — LOW POWER but PORTABLE:**
Batteries are a portable alternative to mains electricity for powering electrical devices. They're great for things like mobile phones and personal stereos, where you don't want to be plugged into the wall. They're also useful for things like shower radios, where it might not be safe to have a mains socket. But batteries are more expensive than mains electricity, and they generally produce less power (see p.103). So, for example, you couldn't realistically use them to run your central heating system.

6) **PETROL AND DIESEL — USEFUL for VEHICLES:**
These make ideal fuels for vehicles (apart from the dodgy environmental effects) but you wouldn't often use them for much else as they're too expensive.

There are lots of forms of energy — but cake's my favourite...

Remember — electricity is so useful around the home because it's so easy to transform it into other forms of energy — if you have all the necessary gadgets, that is. Learn and enjoy.

Using Energy Efficiently

Electrical appliances convert electrical energy into other kinds of energy. Some of this energy is useful and some of it isn't. The efficiency of an appliance is to do with how much useful energy it provides.

Most Energy Transfers Involve Some Waste, Often as Heat...

1) As I'm sure you've figured out by now, useful devices are only useful because they convert energy from one form to another.

2) In doing so, some of the useful input energy is always 'lost' or wasted, often as heat.

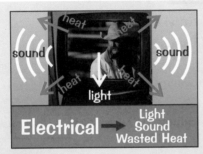

Electrical → Light
Sound
Wasted Heat

The useful energy produced by a TV is light and sound energy. But the TV also gets warm. (If you don't believe me, check for yourself.)

In a kettle, the useful energy is the heat energy of the water. But the outside of the kettle also gets hotter — and heats up the surrounding air.

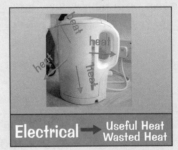

Electrical → Useful Heat
Wasted Heat

3) The less energy that's wasted, the more efficient the device is said to be.

4) The energy flow diagram is similar for all devices, really.

5) The important thing to remember is:

> No device is 100% efficient and some wasted energy is always dissipated as heat.

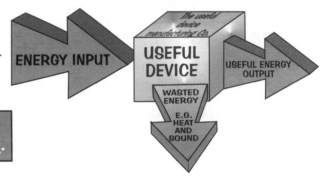

ENERGY INPUT — USEFUL DEVICE — USEFUL ENERGY OUTPUT — WASTED ENERGY E.G. HEAT AND SOUND

...But No Energy Disappears

1) Whenever energy is converted from one form to another, there's always some energy wasted — usually as heat and sound.

2) Take a power drill. Some of the electrical energy is converted into kinetic energy (the drill bit moves pretty quickly) but the drill also gets warm (heat energy) and makes a noise (sound energy).

3) Heat energy from the drill warms up the material that's being drilled into and the air around it — the energy is spreading out into the surroundings.

4) The total amount of energy is the same — it's still all there, but it can't be easily used or collected back in again. (That's why it's often called 'lost' energy. Aaahh.)

Let there be light — and a bit of wasted heat...

So, in a nutshell — useful output energy is always less than input energy, and heat's usually to blame. But remember, no energy has gone — it's just very hard to find. It's much the same as spilling a drink on the carpet — the drink's still there, just spread out all over the carpet and not much use any more.

Using Energy Efficiently

Energy's <u>expensive</u>, and most of us waste loads of it every day. But if your appliances are <u>efficient</u>, you won't waste too much of your money, and you'll be making a start on saving the planet. Good for you.

Efficiency *is Often Given as a* Percentage

1) Here's how to calculate the <u>percentage energy efficiency</u> of an electrical appliance:

$$\% \text{ Energy efficiency} = \frac{\text{Useful energy output}}{\text{Total energy input}} \times 100$$

2) You find how much energy is <u>supplied</u> to a machine. (The total energy <u>INPUT</u>.)

3) You find how much <u>useful energy</u> the machine <u>delivers</u>. (The useful energy <u>OUTPUT</u>.)

4) Write down both numbers — <u>total input</u> and <u>useful output</u>. Then just <u>divide</u> the <u>smaller one</u> by the <u>bigger one</u> to get a value for <u>efficiency</u> somewhere between <u>0 and 1</u> (or <u>0 and 100%</u>). Easy.

> <u>Example</u>: A toy car's motor uses 1000 J of energy to produce 300 J of kinetic (movement) energy. Find its efficiency.
>
> <u>Answer</u>: Efficiency $= \dfrac{\text{useful energy output}}{\text{total energy input}} \times 100\% = \dfrac{300}{1000} \times 100$
>
> $= 0.3 \times 100 = \underline{30\%}$

Some Electrical Devices *are More* Efficient *than Others*

You nearly always have a <u>choice of devices</u> to use in any particular situation. For example, to light a room, you could use <u>filament lamps</u> ('ordinary' light bulbs) or you could use <u>low-energy</u> light bulbs.

Low-Energy Bulbs **are** *More Efficient* **and They** *Last Longer...*

For the same light output, a <u>low-energy</u> bulb is about <u>4 times as efficient</u> as an <u>ordinary</u> bulb. That means they use <u>one quarter</u> of the electrical energy that ordinary bulbs do. So:

1) Using low-energy bulbs could save you <u>money</u>.

2) If <u>everyone</u> used efficient bulbs, we'd need to generate less electricity in the first place — which could reduce damage to our environment.

Energy-efficient light bulbs also <u>last much longer</u>, so:

3) They're more <u>convenient</u> — you don't have to change them so often.

4) If <u>everyone</u> used them, we'd create <u>less waste</u> chucking old bulbs out, and we'd use up <u>less resources</u> and <u>less energy</u> making new ones.

... But They're Not Always the Best Choice

1) Low-energy bulbs are <u>more expensive</u> to buy.

2) Some <u>light fittings</u> don't take low-energy bulbs.

3) <u>Energy efficient</u> bulbs take a few <u>minutes</u> to get to <u>full brightness</u>, which can be inconvenient.

Don't waste your energy — turn the TV off while you revise...

And for 10 bonus points, <u>calculate</u> the <u>efficiency</u> of these machines:

TV — input energy 220 J, output light energy 5 J, output sound energy 2 J, output heat energy 213 J.

Loudspeaker — input energy 35 J, output sound energy 0.5 J, output heat energy 34.5 J. Answers p.140.

Sankey Diagrams

This is another opportunity for a <u>MATHS</u> question. Fantastic.
So, best prepare yourself — here's what <u>Sankey diagrams</u> are all about...

The Thickness of the Arrow Represents the Amount of Energy

The idea of <u>Sankey (energy transformation) diagrams</u> is to make it <u>easy to see</u> at a glance how much of the <u>input energy</u> is being <u>usefully employed</u> compared with how much is being <u>wasted</u>.

The <u>thicker the arrow</u>, the <u>more energy</u> it represents — so you see a big <u>thick arrow going in</u>, then several <u>smaller arrows going off</u> it to show the different energy transformations taking place.

You can have either a little <u>sketch</u> or a properly <u>detailed diagram</u> where the width of each arrow is proportional to the energy (in joules) it represents.

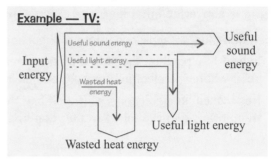

Example — TV:

Input energy → Useful sound energy → Useful sound energy; Useful light energy; Wasted heat energy → Wasted heat energy; Useful light energy

---

EXAMPLE — SANKEY DIAGRAM FOR A SIMPLE MOTOR:

HERE'S THE SKETCH VERSION:

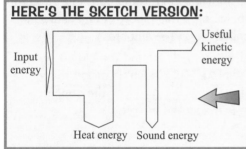

Input energy → Useful kinetic energy; Heat energy; Sound energy

You don't know the actual amounts, but you can see that most of the energy is being wasted, and that it's mostly wasted as heat.

EXAM QUESTIONS:
With sketches, they're likely to ask you to compare two different devices and say which is more efficient. You generally want to be looking for the one with the thickest useful energy arrow(s).

AND HERE'S THE DETAILED ONE:

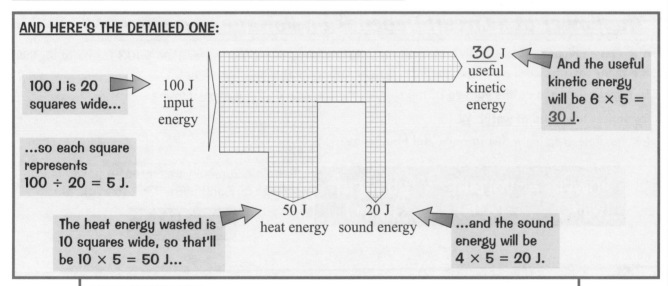

100 J is 20 squares wide...

...so each square represents 100 ÷ 20 = 5 J.

100 J input energy

30 J useful kinetic energy

And the useful kinetic energy will be 6 × 5 = 30 J.

The heat energy wasted is 10 squares wide, so that'll be 10 × 5 = 50 J...

50 J heat energy   20 J sound energy

...and the sound energy will be 4 × 5 = 20 J.

EXAM QUESTIONS:
In an exam, the most likely question you'll get about detailed Sankey diagrams is filling in one of the numbers or calculating the efficiency. The efficiency is straightforward enough if you can work out the numbers (see previous page).

Skankey diagrams — to represent the smelliness of your socks...

If they ask you to <u>draw your own</u> Sankey diagram in the exam, and don't give you the figures, a sketch is all they'll expect. Just give a rough idea of where the energy goes. E.g. a filament lamp turns most of the input energy into heat, and only a small proportion goes to useful light energy.

Calculating Power and Current

There's been a lot about <u>electricity</u> so far in this section, because it's such a useful form of energy. So here it comes again in a bit more detail...

An <u>Appliance</u> Forms Part of a <u>Circuit</u>

Most people in the UK use electricity every day — even if it's just for boiling the kettle and putting the lights on. Then there's washing machines, computers, lava lamps... In all those appliances, <u>electrical energy</u> is converted into other, <u>useful</u> forms of energy (OK, the usefulness of a lava lamp is debatable).

When you plug an appliance into a wall socket, you're connecting it to the <u>mains electricity supply</u>:

1) Two of the 'pins' on the plug are now connected to two copper wires which run through the walls to the point where the electricity supply comes into your house (also along copper wires).

2) This makes an <u>electrical circuit</u> a bit like the one shown below.
    (It's not <u>exactly</u> like this, but you don't have to worry about the details.)

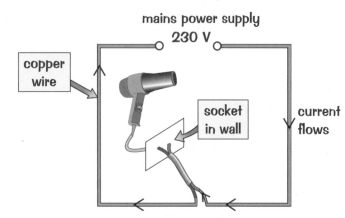

mains power supply
230 V

copper wire

socket in wall

current flows

3) When you switch the appliance on, all the bits of wire are connected up and an electric <u>current</u> (made up of loads of moving electrical charges) flows round the circuit and through your appliance. This <u>current</u> is measured in units called <u>amps</u> (or amperes), <u>A</u>.

4) Current is 'pushed' around the circuit by the power supply. This 'push' is called the <u>voltage</u> or the <u>potential difference</u> of the supply. <u>Voltage</u> is measured in <u>volts</u>, <u>V</u>.

The <u>Power</u> of a Circuit Depends on <u>Voltage</u> and <u>Current</u>

A circuit's <u>power</u> is how quickly it converts electrical energy into other forms (see p.103 for more on this). It's fairly easy to work out if you've got the right information about the circuit.

1) <u>Power</u> depends on the <u>voltage</u> of the supply and the size of the <u>current</u> flowing.

2) Power has units of <u>watts</u>, <u>W</u>.

3) You'll need to learn this formula and practise using it:

> POWER = VOLTAGE × CURRENT
> (watts)   (volts)   (amps)

There's a symbol version too — power is P, voltage is V and current is I (oddly). So:

$$P = V \times I$$

EXAMPLE:

James puts the kettle on.
The voltage of the mains supply is 230 V. The current flowing in the circuit is 9 A.
    Calculate the power of this circuit.

ANSWER: $P = V \times I = 230 \times 9 = 2070$ W.

Circuit training — keep fit while you learn...

<u>Mains electricity</u> is great — you just plug in, switch on and there it is... it's almost magical. Never stick your magic wand in a socket, though. Instead, learn about <u>power</u>, <u>voltage</u> and <u>current</u> — much safer.

Calculating Energy Usage and Cost

When you pay an electricity bill, it's the <u>energy</u> your appliances have used that you're paying for.

Power *is* Energy *Used* Per Second

More powerful appliances use energy more quickly. For example, take a <u>kettle</u>. The <u>higher the power</u> of the kettle, the <u>faster</u> it converts electrical energy into heat energy — and the <u>faster it boils</u>.

1) The units of energy are <u>joules</u>, J.

2) The <u>power</u> of an appliance tells you <u>how many joules</u> of electrical energy it converts into other forms of energy <u>per second</u>. Here's the formula to work it out:

$$\text{POWER (in W)} = \frac{\text{ENERGY (in J)}}{\text{TIME (in s)}}$$

There are two ways to work out power. This one's different from the one on the previous page. (You don't need to memorise this one.)

3) It's important to get the right <u>units</u>. Make sure energy's in <u>joules</u> and time's in <u>seconds</u>.

<u>EXAMPLE:</u>	A drill converts 24 kJ of <u>electrical energy</u> into <u>kinetic</u>, <u>heat</u> and <u>sound</u> energy in 1 minute. Calculate the power of the drill (in watts).
<u>ANSWER:</u>	Energy needs to be in joules. 1 kJ = 1000 J, so 24 kJ = <u>24 000 J</u>. Time needs to be in seconds. 1 minute = <u>60 s</u>. Now use the formula. Power = 24 000 J ÷ 60 s = <u>400 W</u>.

4) The <u>higher</u> the <u>power</u> of an appliance, the more <u>expensive</u> it is to use per second.

Kilowatt-hours *(kWh) are "UNITS"* of Energy

1) Your electricity meter records how much <u>energy</u> you use in units of <u>kilowatt-hours</u>, or <u>kWh</u> (not J). A <u>kilowatt-hour</u> is the amount of electrical energy converted by a <u>1 kW</u> appliance left on for <u>1 hour</u>.

Your electricity meter will look something like this: It shows the total number of units (kWh) used since the meter was fitted. You have to be able to read them for your exam — this one reads <u>5462 kWh</u>.

`0 0 0 5 4 6 2 2` kWh

The red number shows tenths of a kWh — you can ignore that when you're reading the meter.

2) The energy an appliance uses depends on its <u>power</u> and the <u>time</u> it's on for.

3) And yes, there's a formula for it. (It's a rearrangement of the one above, but <u>with different units</u>.)

$$\text{ENERGY UNITS} = \text{POWER} \times \text{TIME}$$
$$\text{(in kWh)} \quad \text{(in kW)} \quad \text{(in hours)}$$

With this one, it's really important to get the <u>units</u> right.

4) If you know how much <u>energy</u> an appliance has used, it's fairly easy to calculate how much that energy <u>costs</u>:

$$\text{Total Cost} = \text{Number of kWh} \times \text{Cost per kWh}$$

<u>EXAMPLE:</u>	An electricity supplier charges 12p per kWh. Find the cost of having an 8.5 kW shower on for 15 minutes.
<u>ANSWER:</u>	Energy = Power × Time = 8.5 kW × 0.25 h = <u>2.125 kWh</u>. Cost = Number of kWh × Cost per kWh = 2.125 × 12p = <u>25.5p</u>.

Convert energy quickly — eat a cream cake then run 10 miles...

You're <u>highly likely</u> to be asked about the <u>energy usage</u> of appliances, and the <u>cost</u> of the energy. So — How much energy does a 60 W light bulb use in 3 hours? Answer p.140.

Revision Summary 1 for Section 2.5

And breathe.

But it's not quite over yet — you've got to check that what you think you learnt actually stuck in your brain. The best way to do that is by answering all these lovely questions. Go on then.

1) Fossil fuels are non-renewable — explain what this means.

2) Give two advantages and two disadvantages of using fossil fuels as an energy source.

3) Describe how energy can be released from uranium in a nuclear reactor.

4) Give two advantages and two disadvantages of nuclear power.

5) Name five renewable energy resources.

6) Describe how hydroelectricity is generated.

7) What are the main problems associated with using wave power?

8) What are the main advantages of using biofuels?

9) State the principle of conservation of energy.

10) Outline the three main stages involved in generating electricity in a power station.

11) How is electrical energy transported from a power station to your home?

12) Explain why electricity is such a useful form of energy.

13) Describe the advantages and disadvantages of the following energy sources:
    a) mains electricity,
    b) solid fuel,
    c) batteries.

14) Write the formula used to calculate energy efficiency of an electrical appliance.

15) Explain why a kettle can never be 100% efficient.

16)* A lamp uses 50 J of electrical energy to produce 4 J of light energy. Calculate its efficiency.

17) Outline the advantages and disadvantages of using low energy light bulbs as an alternative to filament bulbs.

18)* Sketch a Sankey diagram to represent an electric toothbrush.

19) Give the units of:
    a) current,
    b) voltage.

20)*Calculate the power of a circuit if the current flowing is 12 A and the voltage of the mains supply is 230 V. Don't forget to include the units in your answer.

21)* A hairdrier converts 45 kJ of electrical energy into kinetic, heat and sound energy in 1 minute. Calculate the power of this appliance, including the units.

22)*Find the cost of using an electric heater with a power of 30 kW for 45 minutes, if the electricity supplier charges 8p per kWh.

* Answers on page 140.

Heat Transfer

Heat energy tends to <u>flow away</u> from a hotter object to its <u>cooler surroundings</u>.

Heat is Transferred in Three Different Ways

1) <u>Heat energy</u> can be transferred by <u>radiation</u>, <u>conduction</u> or <u>convection</u>.
2) <u>Thermal radiation</u> (see below) is the transfer of heat energy by <u>electromagnetic waves</u> (see p.108).
3) <u>Conduction and convection</u> (see below) involve the transfer of energy by <u>particles</u>.
4) The <u>bigger the temperature difference</u>, the <u>faster heat moves</u> between an object and its surroundings.

Thermal Radiation Transfers Heat by Electromagnetic Waves

<u>Thermal radiation</u> (also called <u>infrared radiation</u>) consists purely of electromagnetic waves of a certain frequency range. It's next to visible light in the electromagnetic spectrum (see p.108).

1) <u>All objects</u> are <u>continually</u> emitting and absorbing <u>heat radiation</u>.

2) An object that's <u>hotter</u> than its surroundings <u>emits more radiation</u> than it <u>absorbs</u> (and <u>cools</u> down). An object that's <u>cooler</u> than its surroundings <u>absorbs more radiation</u> than it <u>emits</u> (and <u>warms</u> up).

3) You can <u>feel heat radiation</u> if you stand near something <u>hot</u> like a fire or if you put your hand just above the bonnet of a recently parked car.

Recently parked car   After an hour or so...

Conduction of Heat Happens Mainly in Solids

1) <u>Conduction of heat</u> is where <u>particles</u> pass on <u>energy</u> (heat) to <u>neighbouring particles</u>.

2) This process continues <u>throughout the solid</u> and some of the <u>energy</u> is gradually passed all the way through the solid.

3) This causes a <u>rise in temperature</u> at the other side of the solid.

4) <u>Metals conduct</u> heat <u>better</u> than <u>plastic or wood</u> — which is why <u>pans</u> are made from <u>metal</u>, but their <u>handles</u> are made of <u>plastic or wood</u>.

plastic

metal

Convection of Heat — Liquids and Gases Only

1) <u>Gases and liquids</u> are usually free to <u>slosh about</u> — and that lets them transfer heat by <u>convection</u>, which is a <u>much quicker process</u> than conduction.

2) <u>Convection</u> happens when more energetic particles <u>move</u> from <u>hotter regions</u> to <u>cooler regions</u>, <u>taking their heat energy with them</u>. (Convection <u>can't happen in solids</u> since the particles <u>can't move</u>.)

3) This is how <u>immersion heaters</u> in <u>kettles</u> and <u>hot water tanks</u> work:

> **IMMERSION HEATER**
>
> 1) <u>Heat energy</u> is <u>transferred</u> from the heater coils to the water by conduction (particle collisions).
> 2) The <u>particles</u> near the coils get <u>more energy</u>, so they start <u>moving faster</u>. This makes the water <u>expand</u> and become <u>less dense</u> — so it rises.
> 3) As the <u>hot water</u> rises, the <u>colder</u> water at the top of the tank <u>sinks</u> to the bottom...
> 4) ...where it's <u>heated by the coils</u> and rises — and so it goes on. You end up with <u>convection currents</u> going up, round and down, <u>circulating</u> the heat through the water.

Heat Transfer in the Home

Owners of homes and workplaces can save money by reducing the amount of energy they use. There are lots of things you can do to <u>save energy</u> in the home or workplace, but some are <u>more effective</u> than others. And some are <u>better for your pocket</u> than others. Some examples are shown below.

Effectiveness *and* Cost-Effectiveness *are Not the Same*

To reduce unwanted <u>heat transfer</u> from a house, you need <u>insulation</u>. There are several types:

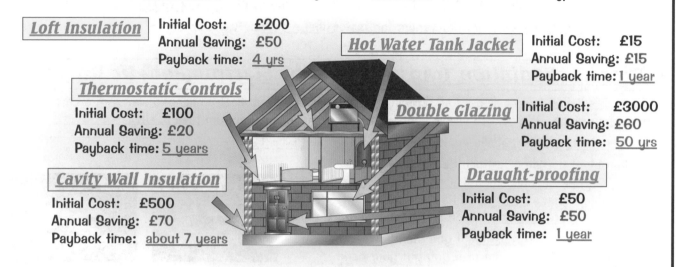

Loft Insulation
Initial Cost: £200
Annual Saving: £50
Payback time: <u>4 yrs</u>

Hot Water Tank Jacket
Initial Cost: £15
Annual Saving: £15
Payback time: <u>1 year</u>

Thermostatic Controls
Initial Cost: £100
Annual Saving: £20
Payback time: <u>5 years</u>

Double Glazing
Initial Cost: £3000
Annual Saving: £60
Payback time: <u>50 yrs</u>

Cavity Wall Insulation
Initial Cost: £500
Annual Saving: £70
Payback time: <u>about 7 years</u>

Draught-proofing
Initial Cost: £50
Annual Saving: £50
Payback time: <u>1 year</u>

1) It <u>costs money</u> to buy and install insulation, but it will <u>reduce your heating bills</u>.

2) Eventually, the <u>money you've saved</u> on heating bills will <u>equal</u> the <u>initial cost</u> of installing the insulation — the time this takes is called the <u>payback time</u>. (The figures given above are just a rough guide.)

3) <u>Cheaper</u> methods of insulation are usually <u>less effective</u> — they tend to save you less money per year — but they often have <u>shorter payback times</u>.

4) If you <u>subtract</u> the <u>annual saving</u> from the <u>initial cost</u> repeatedly then <u>eventually</u> the one with the <u>biggest annual saving</u> must always come out as the winner, if you think about it.

5) But you might sell the house (or die) before that happens. If you look at it over, say, a <u>five-year period</u> then a cheap and cheerful <u>hot water tank jacket</u> wins over expensive <u>double glazing</u>.

Know Which *Types* of Heat Transfer *Are Involved:*

1) <u>CAVITY WALL INSULATION</u> — foam in the gap between the bricks can reduce <u>convection</u> and <u>radiation</u> across the gap.

2) <u>LOFT INSULATION</u> — a thick layer of fibreglass wool laid out across the whole loft floor reduces <u>conduction</u>.

3) <u>DRAUGHT-PROOFING</u> — strips of foam and plastic around doors and windows stop draughts of cold air blowing in, i.e. they reduce heat loss due to <u>convection</u>.

4) <u>DOUBLE GLAZING</u> — two layers of glass means more <u>radiation</u> reflected back, and the air gap between the layers reduces <u>conduction</u>.

5) <u>THERMOSTATIC RADIATOR VALVES</u> — these simply prevent the house being <u>over-warmed</u>.

6) <u>HOT WATER TANK JACKET</u> — insulating material (e.g. fibreglass wool) reduces <u>conduction</u>.

7) <u>THICK CURTAINS</u> — big bits of cloth over the window reduce heat loss by <u>convection</u> and <u>radiation</u>.

It's payback time...

And it's the same with, say, cars. Buying a very fuel-efficient car might sound like a great idea — but if it costs <u>loads more</u> than a clapped-out old fuel-guzzler, you might still end up out of pocket.

Heat Exchangers

So you know that when <u>energy</u> is '<u>wasted</u>', it hasn't really disappeared — it's just been turned into heat. This heat tends to spread out, which makes it hard to capture and re-use. Heat exchangers transfer heat from one place to another in a <u>useful way</u> — either to heat something or cool something down.

A <u>Car Radiator</u> is an Example of a Heat Exchanger...

1) <u>Car engines</u> are designed to convert <u>chemical energy</u> from the fuel into <u>kinetic energy</u>.

2) At the same time as it's doing that, though, a car engine generates an awful lot of <u>waste heat</u>.

3) If the engine <u>overheats</u>, that's bad news for the car, so all cars are designed with a <u>heat exchanger</u> to carry away the heat <u>quickly</u> and <u>safely</u>.

4) This heat exchanger is a <u>radiator</u> that sits just behind the <u>grille</u> at the front of the car.

5) It works like this:

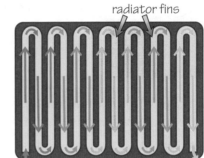

radiator fins

A <u>liquid coolant</u> (usually a mixture of water and antifreeze) flows around the engine and <u>absorbs</u> the excess heat.

This hot coolant is pumped to the radiator — a series of <u>cooling fins</u> that the liquid flows through.

As the car moves, <u>cold air</u> is driven through the grille at the front of the car and over the radiator, <u>cooling</u> down the liquid.

hot coolant from the engine

cooled coolant back to engine

This cooled coolant is pumped <u>back</u> to the engine and the process starts again.

Cars also have a <u>second radiator</u>, which <u>captures</u> some of the wasted heat from the engine and makes it <u>useful</u> again.

coolant · heater core · engine · main radiator

1) This second, smaller radiator is called the <u>heater core</u> — it's used to <u>warm up</u> the <u>inside</u> of the car.

2) The hot coolant is tapped off and sent to this little radiator <u>before</u> it goes to the main radiator.

3) Because this radiator also cools the engine a bit, turning up the heating in your car helps cool down an overheating engine. Weird.

...And a <u>Refrigerator</u> is Another

1) Fridges use some <u>fairly fancy physics</u> to keep your black forest gateaux cold — but luckily you don't need to worry about the details of the science.

2) All you need to know is that a fridge is another example of a <u>heat exchanger</u>.

3) Its cooling system <u>absorbs heat</u> from inside the fridge and transfers it to the room outside (and so <u>cooling</u> down your food).

4) That's why the <u>back</u> of your fridge (where the cooling system is) is always <u>hot</u>. It's also why you need to leave a <u>big enough gap</u> between your fridge and the wall that air can flow through and cool the fridge.

Exchanging heat — go on give me a cuddle...

So, a heat exchanger <u>takes away excess heat</u> and either does <u>something useful</u> with it (e.g. stops you getting hypothermia in the car at Christmas) or <u>disposes of it</u> quickly and quietly without any fuss. Unless, of course, it's my fridge — which has recently taken to mooing like a pregnant cow (ah, well).

Electromagnetic Waves

Electromagnetic radiation is things like light and X-rays. It's made up of waves and is a bit odd, frankly.

Waves Transfer Energy but NOT Matter

Electromagnetic waves (EM waves) transfer energy from one place to another
without moving any matter (stuff). They're all over the place:

A radio transmitter is a source of radio
waves. These waves carry energy from
the transmitter to people's radio aerials.

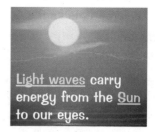

Light waves carry
energy from the Sun
to our eyes.

You can't see EM waves like you can see waves at the seaside. But they're similar in many ways.
All waves have a few basic features that you need to know about:

1) **WAVELENGTH** is the distance from one peak to the next.
   It can be measured in metres, mm or any other unit of length.

2) **FREQUENCY** is the number of waves that the source produces
   per second. (A source is something like a radio transmitter.)

3) Frequency is measured in hertz (Hz).
   1 Hz = 1 wave per second.

4) The frequency is all that makes one type of EM wave different
   from another. E.g. light waves are basically the same as radio waves — but with a different frequency.

The Higher the Frequency, the More Energy the Waves Have

EM waves with different frequencies have different properties — and different uses.
There are seven basic types — shown below with increasing frequency from left to right:

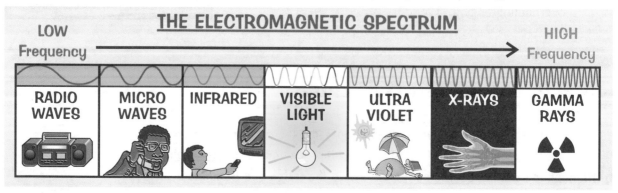

THE ELECTROMAGNETIC SPECTRUM

LOW Frequency — HIGH Frequency

RADIO WAVES | MICRO WAVES | INFRARED | VISIBLE LIGHT | ULTRA VIOLET | X-RAYS | GAMMA RAYS

1) The higher the frequency of the waves, the more energy they have — so, for example, gamma rays
   have much more energy than radio waves.

2) In general, the more energy the wave has, the more dangerous it can be.

EM Waves — not so much fun for paddling in...

The wavelength and frequency of EM waves are related — the higher the frequency of a wave, the
shorter the wavelength. (You can see this in the diagram of the electromagnetic spectrum above.)

Uses of Electromagnetic Waves

Waves with fairly low frequencies are often used for communication — radio, TV, mobile phones, etc.

Low-Frequency Waves are Used for Communication

1) When EM waves hit a substance, three things can happen. The waves might:
   - be transmitted — just pass through the substance, like light through glass
   - be reflected — bounce back, like light off a mirror
   - be absorbed — the wave's energy is transferred to the substance, like microwaves heating food.
2) EM waves above a certain frequency are absorbed quite a bit by the Earth's atmosphere. That's why we use waves at the low-frequency end of the spectrum for broadcasting signals over long distances.

Radio Waves are Used for Radio and TV Signals

There's a range of wavelengths within the 'radio' part of the spectrum. Radio waves can be transmitted round the world in different ways, depending on their wavelengths. (Remember, shorter wavelengths mean higher frequencies.)

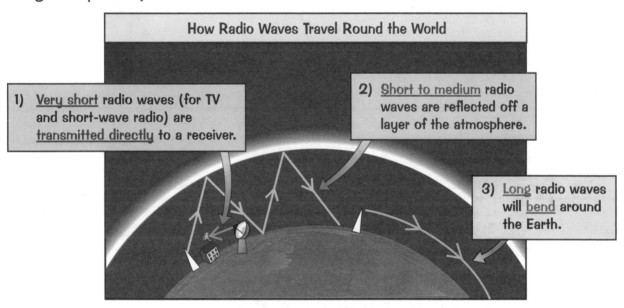

How Radio Waves Travel Round the World

1) Very short radio waves (for TV and short-wave radio) are transmitted directly to a receiver.

2) Short to medium radio waves are reflected off a layer of the atmosphere.

3) Long radio waves will bend around the Earth.

Microwaves are Used in Mobile Phone Networks

When you make a mobile phone call, your phone emits microwaves in all directions.
And then...

1) A nearby mast receives the signal from your phone and passes it on to a central system called the mobile telephone exchange.
2) The exchange passes on the signal to the phone mast nearest to the phone you're calling...
3) ...from where it's transmitted via microwaves to the person you're talking to.
4) There are masts (or base stations) all over the country, so you can make a call wherever you are (unless you happen to live in a small village in Cumbria).

Microwaves — when the Queen can't really be bothered...

Remember, electromagnetic waves come in many different frequencies (and wavelengths) and they behave differently in different substances. That's why EM waves have such a wide range of uses — radio and microwaves for communication, light for seeing things, X-rays for, well, X-rays. Good, eh.

Uses of Electromagnetic Waves

Here come some more uses — now for slightly higher frequency waves like infrared and visible light.

Infrared is Used for Remotes and Thermal Imaging

Infrared waves are used in remote controls, e.g. for TVs and DVD players.

1) An infrared signal transmits instructions from the control to the appliance.

2) Infrared waves are quickly absorbed by most materials. That's why TV remote controls only work if there's nothing blocking the path between them and the TV.

Thermal imaging

1) Infrared energy is emitted by all objects. The amount of infrared an object emits depends on its temperature.

2) Thermal imagers sense infrared energy and create a detailed temperature pattern called a thermogram. This data can then be translated into an image, like this thermal image of three houses. ▶

TONY MCCONNELL / SCIENCE PHOTO LIBRARY

3) This technology lets you 'see in the dark' — warm objects like people stand out from the cooler background.

4) Thermal imagers have lots of uses — they're used by doctors (e.g. to help detect breast cancer), soldiers and emergency services (e.g. for night vision) and in industry.

Fibreoptic Cables Carry Light Waves

optical fibres

Broadband internet uses fibreoptic cables to carry data as pulses of light.

1) These fibreoptic cables can carry vast amounts of data quickly.

2) One cable contains a bundle of many individual optical fibres.

3) Optical fibres can carry signals over long distances using light waves (see below).

Optical Fibres Work by Repeated Reflections

The diagram shows a single optical fibre. This is how it carries signals:

1) A light wave enters one end of the fibre.

2) It bounces off the wall of the inner core over and over again...

3) ...until it emerges at the other end.

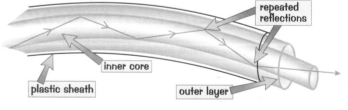

repeated reflections

inner core

plastic sheath

outer layer

4) This process is pretty efficient because very little light 'escapes' from the fibres — so almost all the energy of the wave goes where it's meant to. Compare that to a mobile phone signal where the microwaves are emitted in all directions, not straight to or from your phone — so a lot of the energy is wasted.

5) This makes optical fibres a good way to send data over long distances — the information travels very quickly, doesn't suffer from interference, and is much harder to tap into than an electrical signal.

Fibreoptics — cables with a high bran content...

Optical fibres have loads of uses — telephone networks and cable TV for starters. And they're used in endoscopes — the tubes doctors sometimes use to see inside a patient's body without cutting big holes.

Revision Summary 2 for Section 2.5

Right, it's that time again — so go through the questions and try to answer them all, and if there are any you can't do, blah blah blah. Okay, I'm even boring myself now, so let's have a change. Read each question, and then see if you can rearrange the letters to make a girl's name, a fruit or vegetable and a European city. Please note, this will not in any way help you to pass your exams.

1) Describe how heat is transferred by conduction.
2) Describe how heat energy spreads through the water in an immersion heater.
3) Explain what is meant by the 'payback time' for installing loft insulation in your home.
4) What is cavity wall insulation and how does it reduce the amount of heat lost from a building?
5) Describe how a car radiator system works as a heat exchanger.
6) Give another example of a heat exchanger.
7) Explain the following terms relating to EM waves:
    a) frequency,
    b) wavelength.
8) Name five different types of electromagnetic wave. Which of your choices has the most energy?
9) Three things can happen to an EM wave when it hits a surface — what are they?
10) Which type of EM wave is used by mobile phones?
11) Give two uses of infrared waves.
12) Describe how fibreoptic cables are able to transmit large amounts of data quickly.

The Earth's Atmosphere

At the moment, the Earth's atmosphere contains <u>just the right mixture</u> of gases to keep life going. But <u>human activity</u> can significantly <u>change</u> the atmosphere's <u>composition</u>...

The Composition of our Atmosphere is Just Right for Life

The <u>present composition</u> of the atmosphere is:

> 78% nitrogen, 21% oxygen and 0.04% carbon dioxide (and about 1% other gases)

As it is now, the atmosphere does a pretty good job of <u>supporting life as we know it</u>. You don't need to worry about the nitrogen, but you do need to know why the <u>carbon dioxide</u> and <u>oxygen</u> are so important:

Carbon Dioxide Helps Keep Us Warm

1) The <u>temperature</u> of the Earth is a <u>balance</u> between the <u>heat</u> it gets from the <u>Sun</u> and the heat it <u>radiates back</u> out into space.

2) Gases in the atmosphere (including <u>carbon dioxide</u>) <u>absorb</u> most of the heat that's emitted by the Earth. They then <u>re-radiate</u> this heat in all directions...

3) ...so some of the heat 'lost' from Earth is radiated back towards us.

4) This is called the <u>natural greenhouse effect</u>.

5) Without any 'greenhouse gases', the Earth would be far <u>too cold</u> to support life.

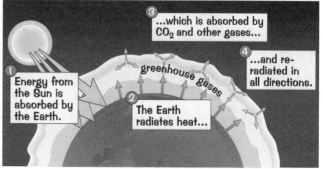

3 ...which is absorbed by CO_2 and other gases...

4 ...and re-radiated in all directions.

greenhouse gases

1 Energy from the Sun is absorbed by the Earth.

2 The Earth radiates heat...

Oxygen is Needed For Aerobic Respiration

Lots of living things respire <u>aerobically</u> (see p.47) — and they need <u>oxygen</u> from the <u>atmosphere</u> to do this. Without oxygen, many organisms (including us humans) would be unable to survive. So, it's pretty darned important to have enough <u>oxygen</u> in the atmosphere.

Human Activity is Changing the Atmosphere's Composition

Human activity is <u>changing</u> the composition of the atmosphere:

1) We're putting lots of <u>carbon dioxide</u> into the atmosphere — by <u>burning fossil fuels</u>, e.g. to generate electricity and run our cars.

2) We're <u>chopping down trees</u> (to make space for growing food and building houses). Trees <u>take carbon dioxide out of the atmosphere</u> (as they photosynthesise — see p.37). So having fewer trees means less carbon dioxide is <u>taken out</u> of the atmosphere.

3) This all means that the <u>carbon dioxide level</u> in the atmosphere is <u>rising</u>.

4) It's not just carbon dioxide that humans release a lot of. For example, the exhausts of cars, lorries, etc. release <u>carbon monoxide</u>, <u>nitrogen oxides</u> and <u>sulfur oxides</u> into the air.

> Changing the atmosphere can have <u>unwelcome effects</u>. Having more <u>greenhouse gases</u> could cause <u>climate change</u>. Too much sulfur dioxide causes <u>acid rain</u> (which damages buildings and poisons trees and lakes). Nitrogen oxides cause <u>poisonous smog</u>.

The right atmosphere — it's crucial at parties...

The atmosphere wouldn't stay the same even <u>without</u> human activity — it changes (slowly) all the time, due to natural processes. During <u>ice ages</u>, for instance, CO_2 levels were much lower than they are now.

Monitoring Atmospheric Change

A change in the composition of the atmosphere could have a big effect on life as we know it.

Scientists Monitor Changes in Atmospheric Composition

Changes in the atmosphere could cause major problems, including climate change and health problems:

1) Climate change could cause all sorts of problems — e.g. millions of people might be unable to grow food if their part of the world doesn't get enough rain.

2) If pollution from vehicles worsens, many more people may suffer breathing difficulties, lung disease, etc.

3) Scientists monitor how the atmosphere is changing — so that they can predict the effects and work out how to minimise the risks. Here are some of the things being monitored:

Emissions from Motor Vehicles and Power Stations

Emissions can often be monitored at the source of the problem.
This helps us control the amount of pollution that's created.

- All motor vehicles have their exhaust emissions tested as part of their MOT.
- Power stations are constantly monitored for emissions of various gases.

Carbon Dioxide Levels

Global atmospheric carbon dioxide levels are constantly monitored by gas analysers. An observatory in Mauna Loa, Hawaii has measured levels of CO_2 since the mid 1950s and its findings are seen as an accurate global measure. We can also find out about past carbon dioxide levels by analysing air bubbles trapped deep in the ice in Antarctica. Clever stuff.

Temperature and Precipitation Levels

Temperature and amount of precipitation (rain, snow, etc.) is monitored every day all around the world. This allows us to see if any changes in climate are happening. Scientists also measure the temperature of the sea surface. This is done from satellites, using instruments which detect infrared radiation.

You Might Have to Interpret Data

In the exam you might have to interpret data on atmospheric composition or on climate change. You might get a graph a bit like this, showing CO_2 levels and global temperature.

Don't panic, there are only a few things you could be asked to do:

1) Read off some values from a graph — this is usually OK, as long as you're careful — this graph has two vertical scales, for instance.

2) Explain the relationship — just state the pattern that you see, e.g. for this graph the two lines go up and down together. In other words, as CO_2 concentration increases (or decreases), temperature also increases (or decreases).

3) Draw conclusions — be careful when you're doing this, e.g. this graph shows a link between CO_2 level and temperature, but it doesn't show that a rise in one factor causes a rise in the other.

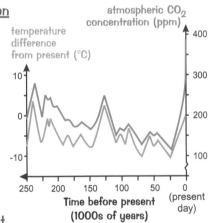

Monitoring the atmosphere — yup, it's cloudy again...

When interpreting data, remember to look really carefully at the details — read the axes of a graph properly, for instance, and get the units of any measurements right.

Tectonic Plates

The ground underneath your feet might seem pretty stable but the Earth's surface is actually <u>moving</u> really, really, really, really slowly.

The <u>Earth's Surface</u> is Made Up of <u>Large Plates of Rock</u>

1) The Earth's surface is made up of <u>tectonic plates</u> — large <u>bits</u> of solid rock which can <u>move</u>.

2) This map shows the <u>edges</u> of the tectonic plates. As they <u>move</u>, the <u>land</u> on top of them moves too.

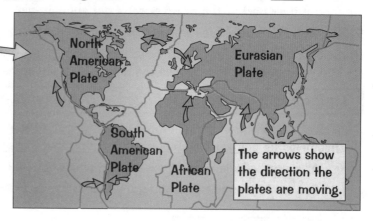

North American Plate

Eurasian Plate

South American Plate

African Plate

The arrows show the direction the plates are moving.

3) Most of the plates are moving at a speed of about <u>1 – 2 cm per year</u>. This slow movement is called <u>continental drift</u> — it's how the <u>continents</u> we know today were formed.

4) As they drift, the <u>plates</u> can <u>crash</u> into each other — <u>creating mountains</u>, e.g. the Himalayas were created this way.

Plate Movement <u>Can Cause</u> Natural Disasters

<u>Volcanoes</u>, <u>earthquakes</u> and <u>tsunamis</u> are caused by <u>very quick changes</u> in the top layer of the Earth. That's why they often occur <u>near where two tectonic plates meet</u>.

1) <u>Earthquakes</u> — <u>shaking</u> and <u>vibration</u> of the Earth's surface resulting from sudden <u>underground movement</u> of the <u>tectonic plates</u> or from <u>volcanic activity</u>.

2) <u>Volcanoes</u> — an <u>opening</u> in the surface of the earth through which <u>molten rock</u> (magma) and <u>gases escape</u>.

3) <u>Tsunami</u> — an <u>ocean wave</u> generated by an earthquake or land slide. They can travel across <u>entire oceans</u> and reach enormous sizes.

Monitoring Earth Movements <u>Can Help</u> Predict Disasters

Scientists have a few tricks up their sleeves for keeping an eye on tectonic plates.

1) <u>Global positioning systems</u> (GPS) are used to <u>detect movements</u> of the plates. This technology is based on <u>satellites</u> communicating with gadgets on the ground — they can detect the <u>slightest</u> movements that we can't see with the naked eye.

2) <u>Seismometers</u> are used <u>on the ground</u> to monitor <u>vibrations</u> and display them as <u>waves</u>.

3) Data from GPS, seismometers, etc. can be analysed to see how the plates are moving.

4) Scientists can also <u>monitor</u> the telltale signs that precede a <u>volcanic eruption</u> — lots of tiny earthquakes, rising magma, escaping gas, increased magma temperature and changes in tilt of the volcano sides.

5) Computers are used to <u>analyse past</u> data to <u>forecast</u> future eruptions and earthquakes. <u>But</u> dormant volcanoes can still <u>erupt suddenly</u> and earthquakes occur <u>unexpectedly</u>.

earthquake

<u>1 or 2 cm a year — that's as fast as your fingernails grow...</u>

<u>Tsunamis</u> are often caused by earthquakes, sometimes underwater ones. <u>Volcanoes</u> can also cause tsunamis — when the explosion causes a <u>landslide</u> into the sea. The Pacific Ocean 'Ring of Fire' — the area around Indonesia — has loads of active volcanoes, and this increases the risk of tsunamis.

The Universe and its Origins

Some scientists aren't content with investigating the Earth beneath their feet and the sky above their heads — it's <u>space</u> that does it for them (or the things <u>in</u> space). The Universe, like the Earth, is constantly <u>changing</u>. Scientists <u>monitor</u> the changes happening now and try to work out <u>what happened in the past</u>.

The Big Bang Theory — the Creation of the Universe

1) Evidence from observations of our Universe suggest that it was <u>created</u> about <u>14 billion years ago</u>.

2) We think that in the beginning, all the Universe's matter and energy was <u>compressed</u> into a <u>very small space</u> — that's <u>all</u> the matter in <u>all</u> the galaxies squashed into a space <u>much smaller</u> than a pin-head.

3) Then it suddenly <u>exploded</u> (in a 'big bang') and started <u>expanding</u> — <u>creating the Universe</u>, including our little planet.

4) The <u>expansion</u> is still going on now — all the galaxies are moving away from each other.

Our Sun is in the Milky Way Galaxy

The Universe is a very, very big place, with many different kinds of <u>things</u> in it (all pretty spread out, mind).

You are here

1) <u>Stars</u> are huge, very hot and very far away. They usually give out lots of <u>light</u> — which is why you can see them, even though they're so far away. Just like our nearest, most beloved star — <u>the Sun</u>.

2) The <u>Solar System</u> is made up of the <u>Sun</u>, some <u>planets</u> and lots of <u>moons</u>, all pulled together by gravity. The Solar System is part of the Milky Way galaxy.

3) <u>The Milky Way galaxy</u> is made up not only by us, but <u>billions</u> of other stars and planets. The Solar System is somewhere <u>halfway</u> along one of the Galaxy's <u>spiral arms</u>.

4) There are loads of <u>galaxies</u> in the <u>Universe</u> — it's really very big.

<u>Astronomers</u> study planets, moons, stars, galaxies, etc. They use telescopes to <u>look closely</u> at objects that are a very <u>long way away</u>. Different types of telescopes are used to detect different types of object, or find out different things about an object. E.g. an <u>optical telescope</u> is fine for looking at the surface of Mars, but an <u>X-ray telescope</u> would be better to 'see' an exploding star.

Distances in Space Can be Measured Using Light Years

1) Once you get outside the Solar System, the distances between stars and between galaxies are <u>so enormous</u> that kilometres seem <u>pathetically small</u> for measuring them.

2) So scientists use <u>light years</u> instead — a <u>light year</u> is the <u>distance</u> that <u>light travels</u> through a vacuum (like space) in one <u>year</u>. Simple as that.

3) If you work it out, 1 light year is equal to about 9 460 000 000 000 kilometres. The closest star after the Sun is about <u>4.2 light years</u> away from us.

4) Just remember — a light year is a measure of <u>DISTANCE</u> (<u>not</u> time).

In the beginning, there was — well, it's so hard to tell...

'How it all began' is quite a tricky problem. Some religious people think that God created the world. Among scientists, the theory of a 'big bang' to get things started is now generally accepted, because that's what the <u>evidence</u> suggests. But we're still rather hazy about if/when/how it's all going to end...

Revision Summary for Section 2.6

It would be quite convenient if the Earth stayed just as it is. After all, how great is a planet that can support bacteria, bananas <u>and</u> baby baboons, and still have left-over resources for us humans... (though this might change, as industrialised society does pretty unspeakable things to large parts of its environment). But nothing stays the same for ever — the atmosphere's changing, the ground's moving and the entire Universe is coming apart. Never mind — <u>exams</u> will be around for a while yet. And the best way to revise for them is still to practise till you're perfect. Talking of which...

1) State the approximate percentages of each gas in the atmosphere:
   a) oxygen,
   b) nitrogen,
   c) carbon dioxide.

2) How is the Earth's atmosphere changing as a result of human activities?

3) Describe the natural greenhouse effect.

4) Why is the oxygen in the atmosphere very important for many organisms?

5) Why is it important to monitor changes in the composition of the atmosphere?

6) How is the current level of carbon dioxide in the atmosphere measured?

7) Describe one way that scientists can work out past atmospheric carbon dioxide levels?

8) Why are temperature and amount of precipitation monitored around the world?

9) How do scientists monitor the temperature of the sea's surface?

10) Roughly how many centimetres per year do tectonic plates move?

11) Describe how 'continental drift' can lead to the formation of mountains.

12) What is an earthquake?

13) Whereabouts on the Earth do earthquakes, volcanoes and tsunamis usually occur?

14) How do scientists monitor the movement of tectonic plates?

15) What is the Big Bang theory?

16) Name the star closest to Earth.

17) Explain why we can see stars, even though they're a very long way away.

18) What is a galaxy?

19) Describe where the Solar System is in the Milky Way.

20) Why are kilometres an unsuitable unit of measurement to describe distances in space?

21) What is a light year?

22) How far is the Earth from the Sun, in light years?

Organisations that Use Science

Science contributes to your everyday life in loads of ways, most of which you probably haven't even thought about — the shampoo you use, the plastic used to make your lunchbox, and even the water you drink are all there because of science organisations...

Organisations that Use Science Can Benefit Society

There are loads of different science organisations and businesses — some make products and some provide a service. Here are some examples of how those products or services benefit society (i.e. you):

By Making Useful Products...

1) DRUGS

Pharmaceutical companies develop, test and manufacture drugs — drugs help us to fight off disease.

2) CHEMICALS

Chemical companies develop and produce things like fertilisers and paint — without these food would be more expensive (and art lessons would be a lot less interesting).

3) FOOD

Food manufacturers grow and process food (unsurprisingly) — they produce large amounts of safe food.

...And Providing Useful Services

1) KEEPING US HEALTHY

The health service includes hospitals, doctors, dental surgeries and pharmacists.

3) ANALYSING CHEMICALS

Lots of organisations have laboratories that do things like make sure the water is safe to drink and make sure products are of a consistent quality.

2) GLOBAL COMMUNICATION

Telecommunications companies make it possible to phone your mate in Australia.

4) EDUCATING PEOPLE

Schools, colleges and universities teach science (lucky for you).

5) PROVIDING ENERGY

Some companies generate and distribute energy — without electricity it'd be hard to do lots of things, let alone watch Neighbours.

These organisations also provide employment for millions of people and large companies generate lots of money for the country. Local organisations are just as important for the local economy.

Organisations may be Local, National or International

1) International organisations have sites in more than one country. They're usually big companies — some examples of those that use science are BP, Unilever and GlaxoSmithKline.

2) National organisations are based in just one country, and they distribute their goods or services throughout the country. In the UK there are organisations like the NHS and the Environment Agency, as well as nationwide shop chains. It's sometimes hard to tell whether a company is national or international, but you should be able to find this out from their website (if they have one).

3) Local organisations that use science include things like schools, colleges, health centres and dentists.

Science organisations — even better than sliced bread...

So there you have it — without a supply of people with science training and skills there would be no science organisations. That wouldn't leave us with very much. So, unless you want to live in a really rubbish future (with no cars, TV or even food), you'd better get learning — your country needs you.

Locating an Organisation

Ever wondered <u>why</u> an organisation is based <u>where</u> it is? Believe it or not, a lot of <u>thought</u> goes into where they're <u>located</u> and it's not just things like, "because it's round the corner from Aunty Flo's"...

There are <u>Lots</u> of <u>Factors</u> to <u>Consider</u>

Not all of these factors are relevant for all organisations, but the <u>general</u> reasons behind location are:

Raw materials

The presence of <u>raw materials</u> required for the process.

EXAMPLE: Breweries are often located next to supplies of <u>pure spring water</u> that is essential for the production of good quality beers and spirits.

Workforce

The availability of a <u>workforce</u> with the <u>right skills</u>.

EXAMPLE: Many high-tech companies (such as biotechnology companies) are based on <u>University science parks</u> because it's easy to recruit employees from the University.

Energy

The availability of an <u>energy supply</u>.

EXAMPLE: Aluminium production is sited in Conwy (in Wales) because <u>hydroelectric power</u> can be readily produced there.

Land

The <u>cost</u> of <u>land</u>.

EXAMPLE: The cost of land in the South East is more <u>expensive</u> than elsewhere — many companies have <u>relocated</u> to the Midlands and up North.

Transport links

Good <u>transport links</u> for delivery of raw materials.

EXAMPLE: Oil refineries are located around <u>ports</u> for supplies of crude oil from <u>tankers</u>.

Market

A <u>market</u> for the <u>product</u> or <u>service</u>.

EXAMPLE: Companies who manufacture dyes tend to be found in areas of textile manufacture.

Grants

Availability of <u>Government</u> or <u>European grants</u> to reduce the <u>start-up costs</u>.

There Could be <u>Effects</u> on the <u>Local Environment</u>

The previous page described some of the ways society benefits from organisations that use science. But because of the type of work they do, some organisations can have a <u>damaging effect</u> on the <u>environment</u>.

1) <u>Toxic pollution</u> — nasty chemicals, e.g. from a chemical works, could contaminate the environment.

2) <u>Visual pollution</u> — some factories and company <u>buildings</u> can be pretty <u>unsightly</u>. Also, things like chemical works and oil refineries are sometimes <u>illuminated</u> at night and are a source of <u>light pollution</u>.

3) <u>Noise pollution</u> — big trucks and big machinery are usually noisy. This can be a big problem for locals if the business operates 24 hours a day.

4) <u>Traffic congestion</u> — large businesses, e.g. a brewery, may need <u>frequent deliveries</u> of raw materials and <u>collection</u> of products — if this is done by road the lorries might cause <u>traffic congestion</u> in the local area and <u>damage</u> to road surfaces.

So you wouldn't put a tidal power station in the Sahara...

You may well be wondering <u>why</u> you need to know all this, well — soon you'll have to produce a <u>report</u> into an organisation, explaining the <u>reasons for its location</u> and its <u>effects on the local environment</u>.

Roles of Scientists

Of the UK's workforce, a massive four million people carry out jobs that use science.
You might be surprised how many different jobs there are in science...

Science Qualifications Offer a Range of Different Careers

This page covers just some of the areas in which scientific skills can be used. There are loads of
employment opportunities for people with scientific skills. There just isn't the space to list them all.

HEALTHCARE — e.g. doctors, dentists, nurses,
pharmacists, radiographers, physiotherapists.
There are also people who support these roles,
e.g. medical physicists and lab technicians.

EDUCATION — e.g. secondary
school science teachers,
university and college lecturers.

ENGINEERING (the development of
materials and technology) — e.g.
chemical engineers develop paints
and dyes, mechanical engineers
develop machines.

SCIENCE
QUALIFICATION

PHARMACEUTICALS — e.g.
research scientists develop,
make and test drugs.

MANUFACTURING — e.g.
analytical scientists are involved
in quality control (making sure
manufactured goods are of a
consistent quality).

FOOD INDUSTRY — e.g. food
scientists develop foods for
supermarkets and food
manufacturers, microbiologists
test food to make sure it's safe.

AGRICULTURE — e.g. research scientists look at
new ways to produce foods or monitor standards of
production, vets keep animals healthy.

There are loads of others — some scientists work for the police as forensic scientists, there are
science editors, scientific patent lawyers, technicians who support the work of other scientists,
goat breeders, orangutan urine collectors, and many, many more.

There are Major, Significant or Small Users of Science

1) Major users of science are people who use scientific skills as a large part of their job. They generally
have a science-based qualification (see next page), e.g. science teachers, laboratory and research
scientists, doctors and nurses.

2) Significant users of science are people who use scientific skills as part of their jobs — their training will
have involved learning a fair amount of scientific knowledge, e.g. science editors and many of the
healthcare professionals (such as dieticians).

3) Small users of science are people who use basic scientific skills as part of their jobs. They don't work
in a science-based job and their training probably wouldn't have included that much science. Small
users include hairdressers (carrying out allergy tests before applying hair dyes and bleaches),
photographers (using chemical solutions to develop photographs), plumbers and electricians.

This is really just a guide though. There are no hard-and-fast rules about putting people into categories
— different people might have different ideas about where they belong.

Rolls of scientists — how does that work then?

Hopefully now you can see that the possibilities really are endless. You could become an engineer, or
even find yourself working as an editor for a company that makes revision guides, sharing your wealth
of scientific knowledge with the young scientists of tomorrow. Still, don't expect that to make your
mam happy — she'll still want you to join the navy.

Skills and Qualifications

Science is a <u>compulsory</u> subject in UK schools until age 16 — after that you can do <u>what you want</u>. Some (usually crazy) people decide that they haven't quite had enough and do even more science after the age of 16. There are loads of different options out there — <u>apprenticeships</u>, <u>degrees</u>, <u>NVQs</u>, the list goes on...

People Who *Use Science* Usually Have *Special Qualifications...*

1) People who are <u>major</u> scientific users will usually have a <u>degree</u> in science. This could be a <u>general degree</u>, e.g. in biology or chemistry, or a <u>specialised degree</u>, for example in forensic science or food science.

2) Some scientists, particularly those working in <u>research</u>, will have a <u>higher degree</u> — this can be either a masters (e.g. an MSc) or a PhD (scientists who have done a PhD are then called doctors).

3) For many careers you have to obtain special <u>professional qualifications</u>. Teachers have to do a <u>PGCE</u> (Postgraduate Certificate of Education), which is a special teaching qualification. People working in the <u>healthcare sector</u> have qualifications that test their understanding of science. They also may have to be '<u>registered</u>' with a <u>supervisory body</u> in order to practise.

4) Many organisations run their own <u>training schemes</u> (often linked to <u>Modern Apprenticeships</u> or <u>NVQs</u>) for careers like technicians and laboratory assistants.

5) Not all people who use scientific skills in their work will need to have science qualifications. This is the case if science skills only form a <u>small part</u> of their job (small users — see previous page).

... And a Wide Range of Skills

On top of <u>formal qualifications</u>, everybody who uses science in their work needs other <u>skills</u> — the exact skills required will depend on the <u>nature</u> of the job, but they might include things like:

1) <u>Research skills</u> — finding <u>information</u> from books, scientific journals or the internet.

2) <u>Communication skills</u> — getting your ideas across in a <u>clear</u> way.

3) <u>Numeracy skills</u> — being able to take <u>measurements</u>, carry out <u>calculations</u> and <u>analyse</u> data using <u>statistics</u>.

4) <u>IT skills</u> — using computer packages, e.g. to make <u>spreadsheets</u> and <u>databases</u>.

5) <u>Planning skills</u> — planning <u>investigations</u> that will be <u>successful</u> and hopefully give <u>good results</u>.

6) <u>Analytical skills</u> — breaking problems down into <u>smaller</u>, easier-to-solve chunks.

7) <u>Observational skills</u> — making <u>accurate</u> and <u>useful</u> observations of experiments and accurately <u>recording</u> results.

8) <u>Applying specialist knowledge</u> — <u>assessing</u> results and drawing <u>conclusions</u>.

9) <u>Team working skills</u> — working as a team is important for a lot of scientific work. Good team working skills will mean that the task can be completed to a <u>high standard</u> in an <u>efficient way</u>.

A typical team of scientists at work — remember, there's no 'I' in 'team'.

Next time you break one of your mam's vases...

...just tell her you were practising your analytical skills. You'll probably need skills like this no matter what kind of <u>job</u> you go for. But you're probably wondering just <u>why</u> you need to know about all this — well, one of the things you have to write about in your <u>report</u> is the <u>skills</u> and <u>qualifications</u> of scientists, so it's going to come in mighty <u>handy</u> for that. Also I thought that maybe you'd just like to know.

Report: Science in the Workplace

Well, now the section's over it's time to crack on with that report I've been blabbering on about.

You Need to Write a Report on Science in the Workplace

This will be the FIRST OF FIVE reports that make up your portfolio for UNIT 3: SCIENCE AT WORK.

Your report will have two bits to it:

1) A discussion of the TYPES OF CAREER that are available in science (you should keep this bit fairly general — don't start talking about specific organisations yet).

2) An in-depth DESCRIPTION of two organisations that use science or scientific skills, including:
   - The work of each organisation — what products they make (or what services they provide).
   - Where they're located (and one reason why) and whether they're local, national or international.
   - The jobs of those employed, what qualifications they have and how they use science.

Start by Finding Out About Science Careers

There are plenty of ways to find out about science careers, e.g. job / career websites, company websites (under the job / career link), your local job centre. Some big employers and science institutions have dedicated careers websites, e.g. the NHS have www.nhscareers.nhs.uk.

Choose Your Organisations Carefully

1) It's no good picking two organisations that are exactly the same (e.g. two international drug companies) — it'd be pretty dull for you and won't get you great marks. Try to pick different-sized organisations (e.g. one local and one international) from different areas of science (e.g. one from healthcare and one from engineering).

2) There are plenty of places you can look for inspiration — e.g. the phone book, the internet, newspapers (local and national), job adverts and the local job centre.

Get Information from Company Websites

1) If they're a biggish company they'll probably have a website. This should tell you loads of the things you need to know, e.g. what they do and where they're located (and if it's in more than one country you know they're international).

2) If you can't find information about your chosen organisation on the internet you might have to write and ask for it. You could also prepare a questionnaire and send it to the organisation.

3) You'll get better marks if you describe things, rather than just stating them — don't just say, 'They make drugs' — instead describe what type of drugs they make and what they're used for etc.

4) When you're looking for information on jobs of the people in the company, it's worth looking out for job descriptions — these tell you what qualifications and skills you have to have to do that job.

For top marks you also need to:
- Explain in detail why the organisation is located where it is.
- Explain its importance to society.
- Explain how the employees' skills and qualifications help them do their jobs.
- Relate the work carried out by the employees to the underlying science.

Writing reports? — I thought this was Science, not English...

There's loads of info out there — the hardest part is knowing where to start. If you're really struggling to find anything about a particular organisation early on then it might be better to pick a different one.

Report: Making a Useful Product

Industrial chemists use many different types of reaction to make products. Chemical industries try to maximise profits by making as much product as possible from the starting materials — a high yield.

You Need to Write a Report on Manufacturing a Chemical

This will be the SECOND report that goes into your portfolio for UNIT 3: SCIENCE AT WORK.

You'll need to make TWO products using DIFFERENT REACTIONS — your report will be in three bits:

1) An explanation of the UNDERLYING CHEMISTRY involved in the reactions:
   • Identify and describe the two different types of reaction used.
   • Write a chemical equation to describe each reaction.

2) Your PREPARATION of the pure, dry products, including:
   • The products — each presented in a suitable sample tube, labelled with its name, date of preparation and correct hazard symbols (see p.1).
   • A measurement of the actual yield of the product.
   • A full evaluation of the procedure used to synthesise each product.
   You'll also need to include a RISK ASSESSMENT.

3) A discussion of the ENVIRONMENTAL IMPACT of your reactions in industry.

Describe the Type of Reaction Used to Make Each Product

There are five main types of chemical reaction used to manufacture products:

1) **OXIDATION** — a substance gains oxygen.
   E.g. when the ore lead sulfide is heated with oxygen, it's oxidised to make lead oxide.

2) **REDUCTION** — a substance loses oxygen.
   E.g. when lead oxide is heated with powdered carbon, it's reduced to make solid lead.

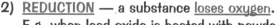
Reduction in a furnace

3) **NEUTRALISATION** — an acid and an alkali react together to produce a neutral compound called a salt.
   E.g. when magnesium oxide neutralises nitric acid, magnesium nitrate (a salt) and water are formed.

4) **PRECIPITATION** — an insoluble solid is formed after two solutions are mixed.
   E.g. mix solutions of lead nitrate and potassium chromate, and you get a precipitate of lead chromate.

5) **THERMAL DECOMPOSITION** — heat energy is used to break up a compound into simpler substances.
   E.g. when limestone is heated it breaks down into quicklime (calcium oxide) and carbon dioxide.

For top marks you also need to explain the underlying chemistry involved in each type of reaction.

Write a Chemical Equation to Represent the Reaction

Chemical engineers use balanced symbol equations to help them decide in what proportions they need to mix the starting materials. You'll need to write an equation for your reaction — do it step by step:

Start with the word equation.   EXAMPLE: magnesium oxide + nitric acid $\rightarrow$ magnesium nitrate + water

For top marks you need to write a balanced symbol equation:

Work out or look up the symbols for your chemicals, and replace each of the words in your equation with its symbol. Then balance your equation.

The balanced equation for this reaction is: EXAMPLE (cont): $MgO + 2HNO_3 \rightarrow Mg(NO_3)_2 + H_2O$

Report: Making a Useful Product

Your teacher will give you procedures to follow to actually make your products. You'll need to do a <u>full</u> <u>RISK ASSESSMENT</u> (see p.2) before you start work — and <u>keep a record</u> of it to put in your report.

> <u>EXAMPLE (cont)</u>: HNO_3 is a strong acid — it is <u>harmful</u> and <u>corrosive</u>. Always wear safety goggles and take care to avoid contact with the skin. Both MgO and $Mg(NO_3)_2$ are <u>irritants</u> — do not inhale, and avoid contact with the skin and eyes. $Mg(NO_3)_2$ is <u>oxidising</u>. Avoid contact with combustible materials (e.g. wood and paper).

Present Your Products Purified...

<u>Purification</u> in your case will probably mean separating a <u>solid product</u> from a <u>liquid</u>.

There are <u>two ways</u> to do that, depending on whether or not the product is <u>soluble</u> (see p.80):

1) <u>FILTRATION</u> — used to separate an <u>insoluble solid from a liquid</u>.

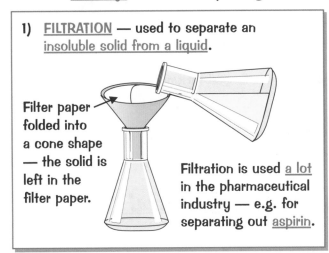

Filter paper folded into a cone shape — the solid is left in the filter paper.

Filtration is used <u>a lot</u> in the pharmaceutical industry — e.g. for separating out <u>aspirin</u>.

2) <u>EVAPORATION</u> — used to crystallise a <u>soluble solid from solution</u>.

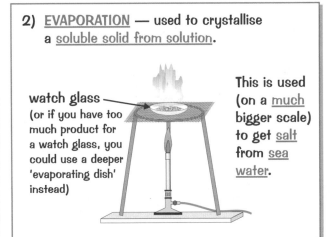

watch glass (or if you have too much product for a watch glass, you could use a deeper 'evaporating dish' instead)

This is used (on a <u>much</u> bigger scale) to get <u>salt</u> from <u>sea water</u>.

> <u>EXAMPLE (cont)</u>: $Mg(NO_3)_2$ is soluble in water, so is purified by evaporation.

...and Dried

Once you've separated out your solid, you need to <u>dry it</u>.

There are <u>three ways</u> of drying a solid product. Which you use depends on your <u>product</u> and your <u>timing</u>:

1) Leave it to <u>dry in the air</u> — this is the <u>easiest</u> and <u>cheapest</u> method. You get <u>better results</u> if there's a <u>dehumidifier</u> in the room, but even so it might take <u>several days</u> to get a dry sample.

2) If you're in a hurry you could use a <u>drying oven</u>. Some drying ovens work just like an oven in a kitchen — they simply <u>heat</u> the sample to dry it.

   You can also get ones that are more like <u>hairdriers</u> — they blow a stream of hot, dry air through the powdered sample. These are used a lot in the <u>phamaceutical industry</u>, because they stop the drug clumping up.

GEOFF TOMPKINSON / SCIENCE PHOTO LIBRARY

3) Or (on the off-chance your school has one) you could use a type of drier called a <u>desiccator</u>, which doesn't use heat. You'd only need to use one for something that breaks up on heating.

> You'll need to <u>weigh</u> your sample at intervals during the drying process (how often you need to weigh it depends on the method you're using to dry your sample). If the mass <u>stays the same</u> from one weighing to the next, your sample's <u>dry</u>. You'll need to make a note of the dry mass of your product for later — there's more about that on the next page.

Chemistry — as much fun as watching magnesium nitrate dry...

It's really important to carry out a risk assessment <u>before</u> you start doing anything — especially in a chemistry lab. Always read the labels on the chemical bottles, wear goggles, tie long hair back, etc...

Report: Making a Useful Product

In industry it's <u>not enough</u> to just make a bit of product and whack it in a tub. You need to know exactly <u>how much</u> product you've made and how <u>efficient</u> your reaction is. It can get pretty technical and there are <u>calculations</u> to do. Great.

Weigh **Your Products to Find the** Actual Yield

The <u>actual yield</u> of a product is just the <u>amount</u> you actually get — makes sense.

> <u>ACTUAL YIELD</u> — the <u>mass</u> of <u>pure, dry product</u> produced.
> It depends on the mass of reactants you started with.

To find the actual yield of a dried product:

1) <u>Weigh</u> your empty sample tube — call that "mass 1".
2) <u>Very carefully transfer</u> your product to the sample tube, then <u>reweigh</u> the <u>full</u> sample tube — call that "mass 2".
3) <u>Subtract</u> mass 1 from mass 2 to give the <u>actual yield</u> that you'll need for your report.

> <u>EXAMPLE (cont)</u>: Mass of empty sample tube = 9.81 g
> Mass of sample tube filled with dried $Mg(NO_3)_2$ = 16.79 g
> So, actual yield of $Mg(NO_3)_2$ = 16.79 − 9.81 = <u>6.98 g</u>

Then Compare **the Actual Yield with the** Theoretical Yield

The <u>theoretical yield</u> tells you how much product you <u>should</u> have got.

> <u>THEORETICAL YIELD</u> — the <u>maximum possible mass</u> of pure product that <u>could</u> have been made using the amounts of reactants you started with.
> It's calculated from the balanced symbol equation.

For <u>top marks</u> you'll need to calculate the theoretical yield yourself. Ask your teacher.

Once you know the theoretical yield and the actual yield, you can calculate the <u>percentage yield</u>.

> <u>PERCENTAGE YIELD</u> — the <u>actual yield</u> as a <u>percentage</u> of the <u>theoretical yield</u>.

$$\text{Percentage Yield} = \frac{\text{Actual Yield}}{\text{Theoretical Yield}} \times 100\%$$

The percentage yield will <u>always be less than 100%</u>. That's because (among other reasons) some product will be lost along the way, e.g. during purification, drying and moving between containers.
If your yield comes out at <u>greater than 100%</u> then your product probably isn't properly dry.

> <u>EXAMPLE</u>: 4 g of magnesium oxide reacted with nitric acid to give an <u>actual yield</u> of <u>6.98 g</u> of $Mg(NO_3)_2$.
> <u>(cont)</u>   The <u>theoretical yield</u> for this reaction was <u>14.8 g</u>.
> So the <u>percentage yield</u> was (6.98 / 14.8) × 100% = <u>47%</u>

And now that's clear — I'm off to yield to the biscuit barrel...*

The percentage yield of a reaction gives you an idea of how <u>efficient</u> your reaction is at converting reactants into products. In industry, chemists work very hard to make the percentage yield as high as possible. This helps to <u>maximise profits</u> and <u>minimise waste</u> — everyone's a winner.

Report: Making a Useful Product

By looking in detail at the manufacturing process for a chemical, it's often possible to find ways to improve the percentage yield.

Evaluate Your Procedures — Why Didn't You Get 100% Yield?

Percentage yield is always less than 100%. Exactly why depends on the type of reaction it is and the apparatus you're using.

You will lose material any time you:

1) Transfer liquids — even if you manage not to spill a drop, some of the liquid always gets left behind on the inside of the old container. Think about it — it's always wet when you finish.

2) Filter a liquid — if you want to keep the liquid, you lose the bit that stays with the solid and the filter paper (they always stay a bit wet). If you want to keep the solid, some will always stay behind on the filter paper when you scrape the product into its sample tube.

3) Heat a liquid — when you heat a liquid, some of it will evaporate.

When you evaluate your procedure, you need to describe its weaknesses. Highlight all the points in the procedure where some of your material might have been lost.

For top marks you need to suggest improvements to the procedure. Could you have done less switching between containers. Could you have used a better separating method? You'll also need to comment on the accuracy and precision of your measuring equipment.

Manufacturers Need to Think About Energy Costs and Waste

For this last bit of the report, you're going to have to do a bit of research into how your reaction works in industry. Your small-scale reaction in the lab will be a bit different from how it's really done.

For ONE of your reactions you need to find out:

1) What raw materials are used? What is the environmental impact of mining / extracting them?

2) At what points in the process are energy inputs needed?

3) What are the waste products? How is the waste dealt with?

You should be able to find out all the information you need from the internet.

EXAMPLE (and we're done):

REACTANTS: A lot of MgO is produced from the mineral magnesite — there are magnesite deposits all over the world. Mining these deposits requires energy, scars the landscape and disrupts habitats.

Nitric acid is made from ammonia. Ammonia is made from hydrogen and nitrogen. Nitrogen is separated from the air, but the hydrogen comes from natural gas (a limited resource).

ENERGY INPUTS: The reaction is exothermic, so it doesn't need an energy input to keep it going. Energy is required to evaporate off the water from the reaction mixture and to dry the product.

WASTE: The only waste product from the reaction itself is pure water, most of which is evaporated off during purification. There are no dangerous waste products.

The highest impacts on the environment from this process come from the mining, processing and transportation of the reactants. The process itself is relatively low-energy and doesn't produce hazardous waste.

Two reports down — three to go...

Right — that's quite enough chemistry for one book. It's time to hang up your lab coat and conical flask, dig out your lenses and voltmeters and get stuck into a bit of physics. Smile — it's not so bad...

Report: Electronic and Optical Devices

In the lab and in your day-to-day life you use a vast number of <u>electronic</u> and <u>optical</u> gadgets — calculators, TVs, contact lenses, microscopes... electronic toe-nail clippers.

You Need to Write a Report on Electronic and Optical Devices

This is the **THIRD** report for your portfolio for <u>UNIT 3: SCIENCE AT WORK</u>.

Your report will be in <u>two bits</u>:

1) A <u>DESCRIPTION</u> of the <u>functions</u> of <u>BOTH</u> electronic and optical devices:
   - A <u>description</u> of the <u>uses</u> of electronic and optical devices and a description of the <u>functions</u> of their main <u>components</u>.

2) <u>BUILDING</u>, <u>TESTING</u> and <u>EVALUATION</u> of <u>EITHER</u> an electronic or an optical device, including:
   - Tests of your device under <u>conditions of normal use</u>.
   - An <u>evaluation</u> of the performance of your device — does it <u>work</u>?
   - Comments on its "<u>fitness for purpose</u>" — is it <u>useful</u> and does it do what it was <u>meant</u> to do?

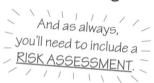
And as always, you'll need to include a <u>RISK ASSESSMENT</u>.

Electronic Devices are Used for Monitoring and Control

<u>YOU CAN MAKE ELECTRONIC DEVICES TO:</u>

1) <u>Monitor and control machines</u> — e.g. monitor the temperature of a machine and light a warning light or shut down the machine if it starts to overheat.

2) <u>Monitor and control physical conditions</u> — e.g. monitor light levels and switch on a floodlight when it gets dark.

3) <u>Control movement</u> — e.g. automatically open a door when somebody steps on a pressure pad or open a set of gates when the circuit senses the headlights of a car.

The delicate <u>monitoring</u> components in these devices need a very <u>low voltage</u>, but the mechanical bits often need a <u>higher voltage</u>. An <u>electrical switch</u> called a <u>RELAY</u> gets round the problem — the low voltage monitoring circuit is used to switch on a <u>separate</u> high voltage control circuit (see p.129).

Electronic Circuits Have Four Main Parts

Most electronic components have one of four <u>basic functions</u> (there are more details on <u>specific components</u> on the next page). You need to be able to identify and describe the function of the:

1) <u>POWER SOURCE</u> — in your case, a <u>battery</u> or <u>low-voltage</u> power supply. There are strict safety regulations for circuits that run from high-voltage supplies (e.g. the mains), so don't build one.

2) <u>INPUT COMPONENTS</u> — these act as <u>sensors</u> to detect what's happening in the surroundings, e.g. thermistors, light-dependent resistors, manual switches, variable resistors, etc.

3) <u>PROCESSORS</u> — these <u>take information</u> from the input and decide the <u>output</u>, e.g. transistors.

4) <u>OUTPUT COMPONENTS</u> — these give the <u>end result</u> of the device. They usually transfer electrical energy into another form of energy, e.g. a lamp converts electrical energy into light energy.

Input — the kettle on...

All the fancy <u>electronic gadgets</u> in cars would get fried if they had the same current running through them as, say, the starter motor. So relays are used to separate the control circuits. Clever.

Report: Electronic and Optical Devices

Electrical Components Can be Represented by Circuit Symbols

Each electrical or electronic component has a circuit symbol that's used to represent it in a circuit diagram (see example on page 129). The ones you're most likely to meet are:

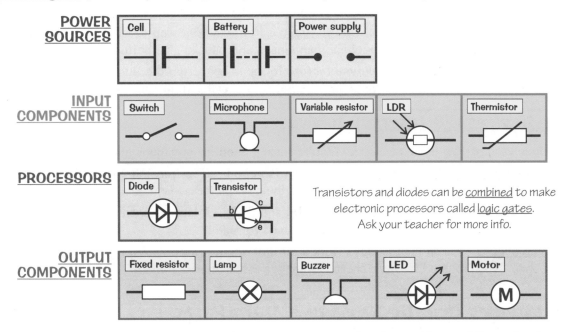

Transistors and diodes can be combined to make electronic processors called logic gates. Ask your teacher for more info.

A **VARIABLE RESISTOR** is a resistor whose resistance can be changed by twiddling a knob or something.

An **LDR** (light-dependent resistor) has a high resistance in the dark and a low resistance in bright light.

A **THERMISTOR** is a resistor with a high resistance when it's cold and a low resistance when it's hot.

A **DIODE** lets current flow freely through it in one direction, but not in the other.

A **TRANSISTOR** is basically a posh switch. If the voltage at <u>b</u> is high enough, the transistor switches on and lets current flow through it from <u>c</u> to <u>e</u>.

An **LED** (light-emitting diode) is a diode (see above) that lights up when a current passes through it.

> If you choose to make an electronic device, for top marks you will need to select the most appropriate power source, inputs, processors and outputs for your circuit.

Optical Devices are Used for Observing and Communicating

1) Some Devices Refract Light

Some optical devices refract (bend) light rays to make an image. They use lenses:

- Cameras — light from the object enters the camera, is refracted by the lens and focused onto the film (or a light-sensitive grid if the camera's digital).
- Microscopes (see p.9) and telescopes — these have two lenses to focus the image of whatever you're looking at onto the back of your eye.
- Spectacles — lenses can be used to correct defects of vision.

Smile — say light-emitting diode...

You don't need to know how all these optical devices work — you just have to be able to give some examples, and explain their important components. Turn over for more exciting applications of optics...

Report: Electronic and Optical Devices

2) Some Devices Reflect Light

Many devices use <u>mirrors</u> and <u>prisms</u> to reflect light to make an image:

- <u>Cameras</u> — in some cameras, a <u>pair</u> of flat <u>mirrors</u> (set up like a <u>periscope</u>) is used to project an image of the shot through a viewfinder before you take the photograph.
- <u>Telescopes</u> — <u>curved</u> mirrors can be used to <u>focus</u> light in a similar way to lenses. Big telescopes use mirrors because they're more practical than lenses and usually give better quality pictures.
- <u>Solar heating devices</u> — these use curved mirrors to focus <u>heat</u> from the Sun onto one point. They can be used to <u>cook</u> with or (on a large scale) to boil water to make <u>electricity</u>.

3) Some Devices Use Lasers

Lasers produce very <u>narrow</u> beams of light. They're mainly used for <u>communication</u>:

- <u>Optical fibre communication</u> — pulses of laser light can be used to transmit <u>information</u> down optical fibres. The information could be anything — pictures, TV, sound...
- <u>Optical storage devices</u> — the fancy term for <u>CDs</u> and <u>DVDs</u>. A laser is used to write the information to the disc, then another laser is used to read it.
- <u>Laser microscopes</u> — laser microscopes work a bit differently from ordinary light microscopes. They're used to make sharp <u>3D images</u> rather than 2D ones.

Optical Devices Usually Have Two Main Parts

Optical devices generally need:

1) <u>A LIGHT SOURCE</u> — this could be <u>natural</u> (e.g. a star for a telescope, sunlight reflected up into a microscope, the Sun for a solar heater) or <u>artificial</u> (e.g. an electric bulb under a microscope, a camera flash, a laser).

2) <u>SOMETHING TO FOCUS OR DIRECT THE LIGHT WITH</u> — e.g. lenses, mirrors or prisms:

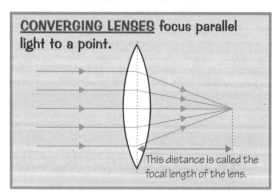

<u>CONVERGING LENSES</u> focus parallel light to a point.

This distance is called the focal length of the lens.

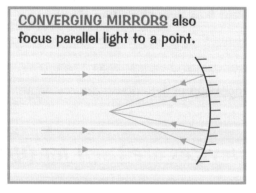

<u>CONVERGING MIRRORS</u> also focus parallel light to a point.

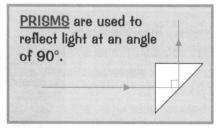

<u>PRISMS</u> are used to reflect light at an angle of 90°.

If you choose to make an optical device, for <u>top marks</u> you might need to use <u>focal lengths</u> to work out where to put each lens or curved mirror. If you're using flat mirrors, you'll need to calculate the appropriate <u>angles</u> to put them at.

Come on guys — focus, focus...

Remember, you only actually have to <u>make</u> one device — either an optical one <u>OR</u> an electronic one. Go for the option that you're most comfortable with. Optical devices are usually <u>simpler</u> than electronic ones, but they're often harder to get just right (in focus, for example). The choice is yours...

Report: Electronic and Optical Devices

When it comes to actually <u>making</u> something, you'll be given a set of instructions.

Diagrams Show How Various Components are Connected

For an optical device, you'll probably get a description of the device, and a simple diagram. For an electronic device, you'll get a <u>circuit diagram</u> instead, showing how to put the components together.

<u>EXAMPLE:</u> This circuit is designed to switch on a <u>warning light</u> and a <u>cooling fan</u> when the <u>temperature</u> reaches a set level. The trigger temperature can be set using a <u>variable resistor.</u>

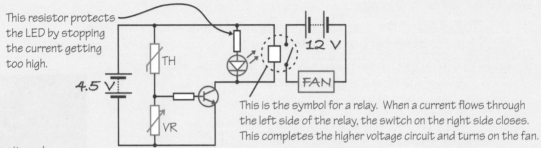

This resistor protects the LED by stopping the current getting too high.

This is the symbol for a relay. When a current flows through the left side of the relay, the switch on the right side closes. This completes the higher voltage circuit and turns on the fan.

Here's how it works:

1) When the thermistor's <u>cool</u>, its resistance is <u>high</u> compared with that of the variable resistor. When that's true, the voltage across the transistor is low, the relay isn't triggered and the light and fan are off.

2) But when it's hot, the thermistor's resistance is <u>low</u> compared with that of the variable resistor. The voltage across the <u>transistor</u> is high, so it completes the rest of the circuit.

3) The <u>LED lights up</u>, the relay switches on the higher voltage circuit and the <u>fan starts</u>. Ta da!

Once you've finished your optical or electronic device, take <u>close-up photos</u> of bits that you're particularly proud of, and a <u>zoomed-out photo</u> of the whole thing. Then <u>label</u> the photographs for your report.

You Need to Test and Evaluate Your Device

When you've built your device you'll need to <u>test</u> it to make sure it <u>works</u>. It's not enough to just <u>do</u> the tests, though — you have to <u>write</u> about them, as you'll need <u>evidence</u> of testing to go in your report.

You'll also need to test it to make sure it works in <u>exactly</u> the way that you wanted it to. How good is it at doing the job? Does it match your specification?

If you'd built the circuit above, you'd want to know:
1) Does the fan switch <u>on</u> and <u>off</u> at the <u>right temperature</u>?
2) Does the fan run <u>fast enough</u> to give a useful cooling effect?
3) Is the warning light <u>bright enough</u> to be seen?

<u>For top marks</u>, you also need to suggest <u>improvements</u> to the device to make it <u>more useful</u>.

If you'd made an optical device, you might want to know:
1) Is the <u>magnification</u> right?   2) Does it <u>focus</u> properly — do you get a clear image?
3) Is the <u>resolution</u> good enough — can you see fine enough detail on the image?

Then for <u>any device</u>:
- Does the device look like it'll <u>last</u> — or does it look ready to fall apart?
- Is it <u>small enough</u> to make it fit for a practical purpose?

How do you test a Dalek? E-VAL-U-ATE, E-VAL-U-ATE... (It's the way I tell 'em.)

If you're building an electronic circuit, it's a good idea to: 1) Test <u>each component</u> before you fit it to make sure it works. 2) Test <u>each section</u> of your circuit once it's built. That way you won't be trying to find faults once your system is complete — the words "needle" and "haystack" spring to mind.

Report: Using Machines

Simple machines in the workplace (e.g. screwdrivers, spanners, pulleys etc.) act as <u>force multipliers</u> — that is, you need to use <u>less force</u> to do a job using the machine than you would <u>without</u> the machine.

You Need to Write a Report _on_ Simple Machines

> This is the FOURTH of FIVE reports for your portfolio for
> <u>UNIT 3: SCIENCE AT WORK</u>.

Your report will be in <u>two bits</u>:

1) <u>DESCRIPTIONS</u> of the <u>uses</u> and <u>components</u> of some simple machines.
You'll have to assemble one of them to use for the second bit of your report.

2) An <u>INVESTIGATION</u> of the performance of a machine, including:

- measurements of the <u>applied force</u> and the <u>force produced</u> by the machine to calculate how much the machine <u>multiplies force</u>.
- a calculation of the <u>work done</u> by the machine.
- a calculation of the <u>efficiency</u> of the machine.

Simple Machines All Work in the Same Sort of Way

All simple machines <u>decrease the force</u> you have to use to move something by <u>increasing the distance</u> you need to apply the force over. Some examples of simple machines are:

1) <u>A SINGLE LEVER</u> — e.g. crowbars, spanners, claw hammers.

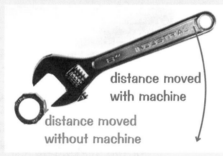

distance moved with machine

distance moved without machine

2) <u>A DOUBLE LEVER</u> — e.g. pliers, scissors, shears (similar idea to the single lever, but you're pushing from two directions at once).

3) <u>WHEEL AND AXLE</u> — e.g. sink taps or wheels for opening doors on ships. The outside of the wheel moves much further than the axle. These are very similar to a spanner.

4) <u>A PULLEY SYSTEM</u> — e.g. a 'block and tackle' on a ship. They increase the length of rope you need to pull to move an object.

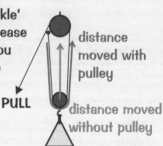

distance moved with pulley

PULL

distance moved without pulley

5) <u>A GEAR SYSTEM</u> — e.g. cogs in a watch.

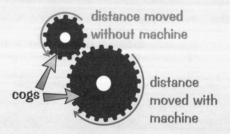

distance moved without machine

distance moved with machine

cogs

As well as increasing the distance the force is exerted over, a gear system can also change the direction of the force.

You'll need to <u>identify</u> any individual <u>components</u> that go to make up these machines. Some don't really <u>have</u> components (e.g. a spanner) but others (e.g. pulleys and gears) do.

> For <u>top marks</u> you'll need to <u>explain the use</u> of these components as well as just identify them.

Report: Using Machines

Once you've put together one of these machines, you'll need to <u>measure</u> the <u>force applied</u> to your machine (effort) and the <u>force produced</u> by your machine (load):

1) You can often use a <u>newton meter</u> to measure the force <u>applied to</u> your machine.

2) How you measure the force <u>produced by</u> the machine depends on its function. You might have to use another newton meter, but there might be an <u>easier</u> way. E.g. if you're using a <u>pulley</u> to lift a load at a steady speed, the force produced by the machine is just the <u>weight</u> (in newtons) of the load.

Calculate How Much the Machine Multiplies Force

This is called the <u>mechanical advantage</u> — and you calculate it using this equation:

$$\text{Mechanical advantage} = \frac{\text{force produced (load)}}{\text{force applied (effort)}}$$

The <u>higher</u> the mechanical advantage, the <u>less force</u> you have to use to move the <u>same load</u>.

> <u>EXAMPLE:</u> You can use a pulley system to lift a load of 700 N by applying a steady force of 165 N.
>
> $$\text{mechanical advantage} = \frac{\text{force produced}}{\text{force applied}} = \frac{700}{165} = \underline{4.24}$$

Calculate the Work Done by the Machine

The <u>work done</u> by a machine is a measure of its <u>useful energy output</u>.
To find it you multiply the <u>force produced</u> by the machine by the <u>distance</u> moved by the load.

$$\text{Work done (J)} = \text{Force produced (N)} \times \text{Distance moved by load (m)}$$

> <u>EXAMPLE (cont):</u> The pulley system lifts the load of 700 N through 12 m.
>
> work done by machine = force produced × distance = 700 × 12 = <u>8400 J</u> (or <u>8.4 kJ</u>)

Machines are Never 100% Efficient

The <u>efficiency</u> of a machine is its useful energy output (<u>work done</u>) as a <u>percentage</u> of the <u>energy input</u>:

$$\text{Efficiency of machine} = \frac{\text{work done by machine}}{\text{energy input}} \times 100\%$$

The <u>energy input</u> is the <u>work done by you</u> as the operator of the machine.

> <u>EXAMPLE (end):</u> To lift the 700 N load 12 m, you apply a force of 165 N and pull through 60 m of rope.
>
> energy input = work done by operator = force applied × distance = 165 × 60 = <u>9900 J</u> (or <u>9.9 kJ</u>)
>
> $$\text{efficiency of machine} = \frac{\text{work done by machine}}{\text{energy input}} \times 100\% = \frac{8400}{9900} \times 100\% = \underline{84.8\%}$$

For <u>top marks</u> you'll need to do these calculations for a <u>commercial device</u> as well as the one you build.

Mechanical advantage — you can fix your own car...

Right — here we go again. All together now... <u>don't forget to do a risk assessment</u>.
And do it properly — even if you <u>do</u> feel like a muppet writing a risk assessment for a spanner.

Report: Monitoring Living Organisms

Scientists monitor organisms to help them understand how the organisms grow, develop and behave.

You Need to Write a Report on Monitoring a Living Organism

This will be the FIFTH and FINAL (hurrah!) report for your portfolio for
UNIT 3: SCIENCE AT WORK.

Your report will have two bits to it:

1) A WRITE-UP of your investigation, including:
   - A plan of your investigation.
   - Your results.
   - Analysis of your results and a conclusion that explains what they mean.
   - An evaluation of your investigation.
2) A explanation of the IMPORTANCE of your investigation in a scientific context.

Plan Your Investigation Carefully

You can't do an investigation without a plan, and a good plan can make all the difference to your marks. Before you start, you'll need to decide:

1) What type of organism you're going to investigate, and what the purpose of your investigation is — what to investigate and why.
2) How to look after the welfare of the organisms you're investigating, and minimise risks to yourself (see pages 1-2 and 133).
3) What conditions you'll be controlling and how you'll make it a fair test.
4) What equipment you'll use to monitor the organism, how often you'll monitor it, and for how long.

This observation hadn't been in Jeremiah's plan

1) Choose Your Organism and Decide What to Investigate

You'll need to CHOOSE what you want to investigate — e.g. you could try investigating:

1) How changing the conditions affects the yield of product from a plant or microorganism.
2) The effects of physical activity on human beings.
3) How changing the conditions affects the growth, behaviour or development of an organism.

In theory you could investigate any organism you like, but you have to be realistic (so lions and wildebeest are probably out). Once you've got an idea for an investigation, ask yourself:

1) Will it fit in with the TIME that's available? If you've only got a couple of weeks for the task, then anything involving the growth of plants is unlikely to fit in.

2) Does my school or college have all the EQUIPMENT I need to carry out my investigation? You might need to speak to the technicians, so they can order anything that isn't in stock.

3) Is the COST reasonable? Nobody likes getting turned down, or wasting their time, so make sure you find out if something's too expensive before planning too much of your investigation.

4) Can I take appropriate CARE of any living organisms that I'm planning to use?

And I had my heart set on a yeti — you win some, you lose some...

These three pages should give you a few ideas about the sort of investigation you could do (as well as what you can't do). The most important thing is to plan your work properly — don't just dive straight in.

Report: Monitoring Living Organisms

2) Think About the Welfare of You and Your Organisms

If you're carrying out an experiment on a living organism, you have to make sure that any discomfort or distress caused is kept to an absolute minimum.

In practice that means you're very limited in your choice of which animals you can use — in fact, you'll probably be restricted to humans. With a human subject, you have to carry out a risk assessment (see p.2) to make sure your experiment's safe, and that both you and your subject know about any potential risks.

The welfare of plants and microorganisms is less of an issue, which makes them much easier to investigate than animals, but you still need to do a risk assessment for your own safety (and marks).

3) Decide What Conditions You'll Vary and What You'll Keep Constant

Whatever your investigation, it will involve varying something and monitoring the effect on your organism. At the same time you'll need to try your best to keep all the other factors constant so that they don't affect the results of your investigation.

Which conditions you vary depends on what you want to find out.

1) If you're looking at the yield of products from, or growth of, plants or microorganisms, you could vary the temperature, the amount of nutrients, the amount of water, or light levels.

> EXAMPLE: Plants need minerals to grow well, e.g. nitrates, phosphates and potassium.
> You could investigate the effect of varying the concentration of one of these minerals. You would need to supply different groups of plants with feeds containing different amounts of the mineral. To make it a fair test, you would have to keep all the other conditions (e.g. light, temperature, water) the same for each group.

2) If you're investigating the effects of physical activity on human beings then you might think about changing either the intensity or the duration of a period of exercise.

4) Decide How, How Often and for How Long to Monitor the Organism

If you're investigating the effects of physical activity on humans, you could measure:

1) Heart rate — by counting the number of pulses in your subject's wrist.

2) Breathing rate — by counting the number of breaths your subject takes.

You'll only need to take measurements over a minute or so, before and after exercise.

If you're investigating growth or yield of product using plants, you could measure:

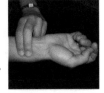

taking a pulse

1) Growth — changes in the height of seedlings or number of leaves.

2) Yield — mass of vegetable or fruit produced.

Plants tend to grow quite slowly, but the rate of growth (and time taken to produce vegetables or fruits) varies from species to species. With a fast-growing plant, you may need to take measurements every two or three days for a period of four to six weeks (depending on the plant).

To find growth rate or yield of product using microorganisms, you could measure:

1) Growth — how the size or number of colonies changes over time.

2) Yield — how much product, e.g. alcohol, is produced in a given time.

Because microorganisms reproduce very quickly you might find you need to take measurements every day or every other day for a week or a fortnight.

> EXAMPLE (cont): A good plant to use would be Brassica rapa — 'rapid cycling brassica'. Plants can be grown from seed in about 4 weeks — growing to around 25 cm tall. You could measure the heights of the seedlings every 2-3 days.

Report: Monitoring Living Organisms

Collect Relevant Data and Record It Clearly

1) Your plan should say clearly <u>what</u> you're going to measure and how you're going to measure it. You'll need to take <u>repeat measurements</u>, and work out <u>averages</u>, to make your results more <u>reliable</u>.

2) So if you're growing plants or microorganisms, you need <u>more than one</u> plant or culture plate for <u>each set of conditions</u>. If you're investigating the effect of activity on a human you'll need to get them to <u>repeat the activity</u> several times so you can take repeat measurements — lucky subject.

3) <u>Check</u> any results that look weird by repeating part of the investigation.

4) The best way to present your results is to use <u>tables</u> and <u>graphs</u> to show any <u>trends</u> in the data.

<u>EXAMPLE (cont)</u>: If you were measuring the growth of *Brassica rapa* seedlings at different concentrations of nitrate, you might record your data like this:

Concentration of nitrate (mg/l)	Height of seedlings after 7 days (mm)			
	Seedling 1	Seedling 2	Seedling 3	Average
0.1	51	49	50	50
0.2	57	54	55	55.3

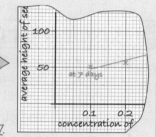

You might want to gather the same sort of data at, e.g., 14 days, 21 days and 28 days, and plot them separately on the graph. <u>For help with tables and graphs, see pages 26-27</u>.

Analyse Your Results and Evaluate Your Investigation

<u>ANALYSING</u> your results (see p.28 - p.30) means you have to:

Look for <u>trends</u> and <u>patterns</u> in your data. Draw <u>conclusions</u>, based on the trends, to <u>explain</u> your results using <u>scientific knowledge</u> and <u>understanding</u>.

<u>EVALUATING</u> your investigation (see p.30) means you have to think about:

What went <u>well</u>, what <u>didn't</u> go so well and <u>why</u>. How you might <u>improve</u> the investigation in the future. Whether there's anything you could do <u>differently</u> to get more <u>reliable results</u>.

Explain the Scientific Importance of Your Investigation

<u>MONITORING THE HUMAN BODY</u> is essential in the <u>diagnosis</u> and <u>treatment</u> of disease. Measurements of <u>breathing rate</u> and <u>heart rate</u> are used as part of general health checks, as well as to help <u>athletes</u> monitor their fitness for training. Other measurements, like blood sugar levels and blood pressure, are used to monitor specific disorders.

<u>MONITORING THE GROWTH AND DEVELOPMENT OF PLANTS</u> is very important in <u>agriculture</u>. Agricultural scientists work very closely with <u>crop farmers</u> and <u>nurseries</u> to work out what conditions plants need for <u>healthy growth</u> and <u>maximum yield</u>.

<u>MONITORING MICROORGANISMS</u> has lots of applications — from developing <u>new drugs</u> to <u>brewing beer</u>. Some microbiologists work with <u>genetically modified</u> bacteria to produce <u>useful products</u>, e.g. human insulin. They have to make sure the conditions are just right to produce the <u>maximum yield</u>.

<u>EXAMPLE (the end)</u>: Experiments like this are used to find the perfect combination of nutrients for each crop. The end result is a high yield of good quality crops for the farmer to sell and plenty of cheap food for the consumer.

Babysitting — monitoring microorganisms...

A couple of tips: 1) Use <u>neat tables</u> for your data right from the start. Don't just scribble on a scratty bit of paper towel "to write up later" — that's how you lose results. 2) Use a biro — lovely, fountain-penned tables are a bit hard to read after some numpty's spilt a beaker of liquid fertiliser over them.*

Tips on Producing Your Portfolios

Even if you think this stuff is <u>blindingly</u> obvious, <u>READ IT</u> anyway — humour me.
It's a list of the stuff you <u>must</u> remember when you're putting your portfolios together...

You'll Need a Portfolio for *Each Coursework Unit*

1) You'll have to produce <u>two separate portfolios</u> — one each for <u>Unit 1</u> and <u>Unit 3</u>.

2) For each unit, you'll have to write various <u>reports</u> (see pages 6, 31, 121 and 122-134 for specific advice on the reports).

3) The portfolios are marked by your <u>teacher</u> and moderated by OCR.

4) The portfolios make up <u>two thirds</u> of your final grade, so they're pretty important...

I'm not impressed

Your Portfolios Should be *Neat* and *Easy to Follow*

If you hand in a <u>jumbled</u>, <u>illegible mess</u> and call it a portfolio, your teacher will <u>NOT</u> be impressed.

1) Your portfolios should be <u>well organised</u>, <u>well structured</u> and <u>tailored</u> to the tasks (so no random notes from lessons, no unidentified graphs or diagrams, no pictures of Elvis).

2) If you've got access to a computer, <u>word process</u> your reports — they're much <u>neater</u> that way, and it's easier to <u>edit</u> your work if you change your mind about something.

3) Make life easy for your marker — break up your report with <u>headings</u> to make it easier to follow.

4) If you're including any <u>graphs</u>, <u>diagrams</u> or <u>photos</u>, make sure they're clearly <u>labelled</u>.

5) There's no right or wrong <u>length</u> for a report. But they should be only as long as they <u>need to be</u> to cover everything. Don't <u>pad them out</u> for the sake of it — no one likes wading through waffle.

6) <u>Read through</u> your work carefully before handing it in (run a <u>spellcheck</u> if you're using a computer).

Make Sure It's *All Your Own Work*

Make sure there's nobody else's work in with yours. <u>I</u> know you're honest, but OCR take a very dim view of two candidates' work being <u>too similar</u>.

It's fine to include bits in your reports that come from <u>books</u> or <u>websites</u>, but you need to <u>reference</u> them — say where they come from. Your references can go at the <u>end</u> of the report.

You also need to work as <u>independently</u> as possible. The more <u>help</u> you need from your <u>teacher</u>, the lower your mark. But, saying that, it's better to do something with help than just miss it out altogether.

And Then for a Few *Finishing Touches*

Clear presentation makes your portfolio <u>easier to follow</u>... which makes life easier for the person <u>marking</u> it... which puts them in a <u>good mood</u>... which has got to be good. Here are a <u>few tricks</u>:

1) Make a <u>front cover</u> for your portfolio. It should have <u>your name</u>, the <u>course name</u> and the <u>unit number and title</u>. (There's an official cover sheet to go in front of this as well — ask your teacher.)

2) Separate the different reports with <u>header pages</u> — nothing fancy, just put the name of the report.

3) <u>Number</u> your pages. Call the first header page "page 1", then just <u>number through</u> to the end.

4) Include a <u>contents page</u> with page numbers.

5) Hole-punch everything and put it in a <u>ring binder</u>... and you're done. Woohoo!

Index

Index

Index

Index

Index and Answers

Answers

Revision Summary for Section 2.3

1) 1

8) 9

9) Silicon

10) 7

14) a) organic, b) inorganic, c) inorganic

Revision Summary for Section 2.4

31) a) metal

  b) reinforced concrete

  c) ceramic, e.g. porcelain

  d) ceramic or heat-resistant polymer

  e) metal, e.g. copper

  f) ceramic or melamime

Bottom of page 100

TV: (7 ÷ 200) × 100 = 3.5%

Loudspeaker: (0.5 ÷ 35) × 100 = 1.4%

Bottom of page 103

Energy = Power × Time
= 0.06 kW × 3 h
= 0.18 kWh

Revision Summary for Section 2.5

16) Efficiency = (4 ÷ 50) × 100 = 8%.

18) Your diagram should look similar to the example shown below:

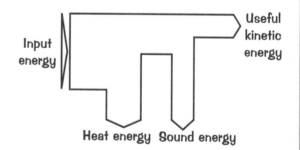

20) Power = 230 × 12 = 2760 W.

21) Power = 45 000 ÷ 60 = 750 W.

22) Energy units = 30 × 0.75 = 22.5 kWh.
Total cost = 22.5 × 8 = 180p or £1.80.